Ainslie Meare
by O

MW00846799

Relief Without Drugs* by Ainslie Meares
Samples of Poems⁺ by Ainslie Meares

Dedication
To all Meares' Stillness Meditation teachers who are spreading something precious and who should be encouraged.

To my family (including the Capital Letter Queen) for reading various drafts and patiently allowing its completion.

Disclaimer
It may be hazardous to heath not to relax and live in a calm way.

You, the reader, have a responsibility to seek out and listen to the best advice available. Follow sensible advice. Disregard advice which is the opposite. This all applies to this book. This book is intended for general information only. It should not be used as a substitute for consulting a qualified health practitioner. Neither the author nor the publisher can accept any responsibilty for your health or any side effects of methods in this book.

ISBN 978-0-646-96693-9

Cover, graphic design & photograph restoration. Sarah **Bruhn**

Table of Contents

Foreword

Many who pick up this book will do so because they remember the innovative work of Dr Ainslie Meares across a range of psychological and physiological interventions. Many will attribute life transformation to his ideas and 'way of doctoring' and are grateful; many know his name and would like to learn more, and some less informed may well have argued against him. Regardless of readership, this work is a testimony to Meares' genius as he opened doorways in the Western world to the recognition of meditation as a practice for wellness – and also to what we now know as mind-body medicine.

In **Ainslie Meares on Meditation** Owen Bruhn provides a summary of information on this topic for 21stC readers. An avid and competent researcher and committed advocate of Meares' work, Bruhn's condensation of this substantial task is admirable. Within this book you will discover Meares' writings from his earliest through to those written close to his passing in 1986. Among these, Owen Bruhn has also discovered a range of Meares' little known writings and publications previously difficult to source, along with observations of value but not necessarily part of the essence of his final teaching.

Included in this book is a distilled version of Meares' classic **Relief Without Drugs**, written for the public and first published in the U.S.A. in 1967. That work is still sought after and very difficult to purchase today so **Ainslie Meares on Meditation** provides a significant section of that knowledge. Section 3 of Bruhn's book summarises Meares' entire body of work on meditation and includes an overview of the typical exercises suggested for those without access to a teacher together with Meares' inimitable style of 'making the stillness experience more general'.

Ainslie Meares' work evolved via an extraordinary and diverse journey to reach its end point. In his book Owen Bruhn has kindly given credit to me in following that tradition. While my work and my writings on Stillness Meditation Therapy authentically replicate Meares' core teaching, this book by Owen Bruhn provides the map, the way by which Meares arrived at his conclusive style of meditation. I highly recommend this book to all who aim to live and teach 'a better life'.

Pauline McKinnon, Melbourne 2017

Background

I remember hearing about Ainslie Meares' work in the media from perhaps 1970 onwards. Eventually, I realised that this eminent doctor, meditation researcher and teacher worked in the same city I lived in. I decided to find out if he would teach me that which I felt was missing from my own exploration of eastern arts. He granted my request. During my attendance at his classes I witnessed his last step to simpler prompts (discussed in book). Back in mid-1984 it was a change I accepted and thought no more about.

In recent years, I sustained an uncomfortable injury. Various physical treatments did little but, use of the principles of the Egoscue method stabilised my injury and has helped maintain a good quality of movement. Eventually, someone suggested I try visualising relaxation and I decided to verify my meditation practice.

This is where the story really begins, in 2014, after I attended the Stillness Meditation Therapy Centre. This deepened my own practice and reinvigorated my interest - which only increased after I commenced the SMT® teacher training course. I already had about 20 of Meares' books and acquired copies of the rest as well as all his articles – if any were missed they were pretty well hidden. So began a bibliography. At the repeated suggestions of others this became a book about the man and his method.

Ainslie Meares on Meditation is the title as it is his story and his work. Indeed, the distilled version of his book, **Relief Without Drugs (RWD)** and samples of his poetry form part of the book.

Our ancestors were hunter gatherers for a million years, learnt agriculture 10,000 years ago, then came the city, technology and computers. Looking back, makes the pace and extent of change clearer. If anything, it is increasing. Adverse health effects occur if our living conditions depart too far from the evolutionary blueprint including diet, posture, physical activity, etc.

Nature intended that humans take a few minutes of profound mental rest daily and let this flow on so as to live a calm and better, busy life. This is our birth right – it is Meares' method in a nutshell.

Read on and read deeply. But, appreciate that reading about Stillness Meditation is not the same as experiencing it. Meares wrote at various times that: *it is only doing that really counts.*

Outline

S1. About Ainslie Meares

Section 1 (S1) outlines Meares' life and the development of his method drawing on his publications and other sources. It also serves as a guide to his 34 books to help you identify which might be of most interest. Many of his major articles are footnoted here and in other sections. Living relatives are not mentioned for reasons of privacy.

S2. Relief Without Drugs By Ainslie Meares, MD

Section 2 is a distilled version of **Relief without Drugs (RWD)** by Ainslie Meares that contains the essence of that book. It is a snapshot of Meares method in the 1960s. Meares wrote for the audience of the time using language they would understand, it was politically correct back then but, today readers should bear this in mind. Short summaries of the Relaxing Mental Exercise and Meares' Notes on Pain have also been added. Don't forget that pain serves as a warning – always be quite clear about what is causing pain before relieving it.

S3. Stillness Meditation

Like any researcher at the leading edge, Meares worked on improving and fine tuning his method. S3 provides an overview of Stillness Meditation "**After RWD**" and adopts Pauline McKinnon's plain language terms. It also discusses Meares' ideas on "making the stillness more general" and living calm in daily life.

S4. Meares' Therapeutic Poetry

Samples of Meares' poems, most previously disclosed by others, have been placed in one section rather than scattering them through the book. The samples are drawn from all his poetry books to enable the reader to taste the flavours and help work out which books to get. Meares thoughts on the benefits and use of his poetry are discussed at the end of S3.

S5 Ainslie Meares' Personal Practice

People ask "what were Meares own protocols and personal practices?". This section answers that question.

S6. Learn, Experience & Live Calm

S5 provides a summary of Meares' Stillness Meditation and living calm. It also includes Meares' recommendations about his own books and mentions some books by other authors.

1. About Ainslie Meares

An Occupational Biography of Ainslie Meares MD, BAgrSc, DPM.

1.1 The Early Years

Ainslie Dixon Meares was born on 3 March 1910, at Sandringham, Melbourne, Australia. His family came from a successful background with his father having been a gentleman doctor. Meares was taught by a governess until 10 years old and subsequently attended Melbourne Grammar School. He was a shy, sensitive child, who boxed and played tennis as he grew up into a tall, lean youth. However, he had become a school prefect by 1928. That year he was orphaned due to the death of both parents from illness. He toured India and Tibet with the school around that time and was confronted by both the exotic nature and the poverty of Asia. He did not meet with any yogis although as a tourist he may have seen some.

After leaving school, Meares spent a year working on country properties owned by a relative before attending the University of Melbourne. He completed a degree in Agriculture in 1934, with the idea in mind of becoming a gentleman farmer. That same year he married his wife Bonnie (nee Byrne). On their honeymoon in Europe she encouraged him to undertake further study and he returned to the University to study medicine. Meares came from a well off background and had no pressing need to work. For him medicine was something to do that was worthwhile and would be of interest.

In 1936, the couple built a house on a farm near Heidelberg which is now a suburb of Melbourne. They called the house, Aldermaston, after the location in England where they had stayed on their honeymoon. The house was modelled on Meares recollections of his childhood family home.

A few year later, the Army purchased land adjacent to Aldermaston. That land was turned into Army "Camp Q" and became commonly known as Watsonia Barracks. In 1951[1], the Army purchased Aldermaston and all the accompanying land. The Meares and their three children moved to another suburb. The farm became a military medical training camp and Aldermaston was, for a short period, a hospital. Today, the camp remains a military base, Simpson Barracks, that is closed to the public.

Meares completed his medical degree and joined the armed forces in October 1941[2]. Shortly after, he was appointed a captain in the Australian Army Medical Corps. At one point, he was located at Camp Q whilst his family was at Aldermaston! He spent most of the war serving in Australia. In 1944, he spent 4 months in New Guinea.

---

1 Riverina Herald, 24 Oct 1951, p6
2 Service Record No. VX64992, Aust Military Forces.

1.2 Hypnosis Period

Hypnotherapy

On his return from New Guinea in late 1944, the army sent Meares to Unit 114, a military mental hospital, in Goulburn, New South Wales, where he remained until he left military service after the war ended. The hospital was full of traumatised troops whose wartime experience had broken their minds. It was Meares job to put them back together again. Meares was introduced to conventional therapies including the use of drugs and shock treatment as well as the new field of medical hypnosis. Meares left the army towards the end of 1946 and completed his diploma in psychological medicine in 1947. He worked in psychiatric positions in Melbourne Teaching hospitals, at first full time and later part-time. This reduction to part-time occurred as by 1950 he had begun a private psychiatric practice – initially in a partnership, which finished shortly after the sale of Aldermaston.[3] From 1952 he practised by himself. His work included some forensic psychiatry - he told one court[4] that he did not like such work as he put the interests of his patients first and the court might not necessarily do that; going on to agree that he was a citizen who understood the rule of law but he was a doctor first and foremost.

Soon after Meares started work in psychiatry he became involved in the new and controversial field of hypnotic psychiatry. From the outset of his career, Meares had to deal with doubt and misunderstanding from colleagues who knew much less about the topic than himself. These colleagues only knew of "theatrical" hypnosis, in which highly suggestible people are encouraged to do foolish things for the entertainment of the audience. Two decades later, comparing himself with other psychiatrists, Meares[5] said that working continuously with hypnotized patients had given him very different insights into workings of the mind. At the start, many of his colleagues who did not use hypnosis misunderstood Meares' work, and as his knowledge and experience grew the gap only increased.

Meares researched and used hypnotic painting[6] to enable patients to communicate deep conflicts not identified by other techniques. He wrote a book about one case where he used paintings made by a lonely, severely afflicted schizophrenic patient to

---

3 The Melbourne Age, 27 Feb 1952, p2
4 The Melbourne Age, 20 May 1950, p3
5 Proc Medical Legal Society Victoria V11:73-84. 1967
6 Hypnography; also reported in J Mental Sci V100(421): 965–974. 1954

communicate with and help her cure herself.[7] After learning of this work Cunningham Dax, a fellow psychiatrist, wrote *"Few psychiatrists have the courage to take us through their own experiences, particularly with so subjective and intimate an approach"*. The Age said his *"sympathy and intuition make him much more than a doctrinaire psychiatrist"*

Meares invented and developed methods using clay modelling under hypnosis[8] so deep that the patient could not talk but could model *"the thing in their mind'*. The depth of hypnosis was needed to facilitate the process of hypnoanalysis (as it was called). This is also indicative of his skill as a medical hypnotist.

The development of these techniques also sees Meares mentioned as an early innovator in art and occupational therapy. However, they were a minor side road compared to the work he did refining and developing techniques in patient communication and hypnosis. Meares researched many approaches and techniques used to communicate with and\or to hypnotise the patient. **The Medical Interview**, was specifically about the process of communication between doctor and patient[9]. A few years later his summary of the "channels of communication" was published in the Lancet[10].

In 1957, he completed his Doctorate of Medicine[11] which included 16 journal publications in the area of hypnosis covering much of the work mentioned above. By 1960, he had documented all of it and more in a 500 page long textbook **A Medical System of Hypnosis** that included a summary of his new theory of hypnosis.

His work in hypnosis, including his new theory of hypnosis, was a major achievement and was well recognised by specialist colleagues in Australia and overseas. Some later referred to him as a "wizard of hypnosis"[12]. He was President of the International Society of Hypnosis[13] in 1961-1962, having been invited to join it a decade earlier.[14] He was an assistant technical editor for the Society's journal from around 1964 until 1977[15]. Meares was one of 39 Foundation Fellows of the Royal ANZ College of Psychiatrists appointed based on professional standing, eminence, and distinction in literature

7 Door of Serenity
8 Shapes of Sanity
9 The Medical Interview
10 Lancet 275(7126): 663–667. 1960
11 MD Thesis, Uni of Melbourne, Dept Medicine & Dentistry 1957
12 Kihlstrom, J (1999) Hypnosis Research in Aust. Ann Meeting APS
13 Watkins, JG (1995) Int J clin Exp Hypnosis 43(3)332-341;
14 Schneck, JM (1993) Int J Clin Exp Hypnosis 41(3): 169-171
15 Listed in each issue of Int J Clin Exp Hypnosis

science.[16] Other affiliations included: Member of the Medico-Legal Society of Victoria[17], Member of the World Psychiatrists Association, Fellow of the American Society for Clinical Hypnosis, Member of the American Psychiatric Association and Member of the Royal Medico-Psychological Association[18] (ie the Royal College of Psychiatrists)[19].

States Of Hypnosis And Healing

From the start of his career, Meares emphasised that it was not the doctor who healed the patient. The doctor merely provided the circumstances that permitted the patient's own natural healing mechanisms to work most efficiently and effect a cure. For example, in the case of a fracture, the doctor aligned the bones and placed the damaged limb in a cast which then allowed the fracture to mend. The mind, he said, was no different, if anxiety had fractured the mind then it was the doctor's job to help the patient's own natural mechanisms to work better to mend the mind. The mind and body's ability to cope with changes is sometimes referred to as homeostasis. Homeostasis means keeping things constant and comes from two Greek words: 'homeo,'or 'similar,' and 'stasis,' or 'stable.' So, homeostasis is self regulation of the human mind and body so as to maintain a stable, relatively constant condition. If an organism's state changes then a homeostatic mechanism shifts it back towards the normal state. If the stimulus is sufficient to result in adverse effects then the mechanism shifting the state towards normal is one of restoration and healing.

Earlier medical hypnotists had the idea that hypnosis involved a primitive state. Meares had noted that deeply hypnotised subjects only painted with one colour suggesting that colour vision was reduced or absent. He knew that deep hypnosis could inconveniently involve the subject temporarily losing the ability to talk. Speech returned as the hypnosis became less deep.

It was in 1957 that Meares[20] put forward the idea that subjects deep in hypnosis were temporarily shifting, or regressing, back to a simpler more primitive mode. A mode that included simple communication by suggestion such as would have been experienced by remote primitive ancestors. The process of a **temporary** step back to an older simpler state of mind he described as an atavistic regression. Attavus is Latin for remote ancestor. Literally, it means forefather or the grandfather of the grandfather. It describes those

16 Rubinstein, WD & HL(1996) Menders of the mind: a history of the Royal ANZ College of Psychiatrists, 1946–96

17 Proc Med Legal Soc Vic 7:137-151,1956; 11:73-84,1967; 12: 277-284, 1973

18 Victorian Parliamentary Report No 1. 6502-1965, p178

19 http://www.rcpsych.ac.uk/usefulresources/thecollegearchives.aspx

20 AMA Archives Neurol & Psych 77(May):549–555. 1957

earlier generations going back to remote times. So, the regression could also be termed ancestral, primal or primordial as it is a going back to an earlier stage of the evolution of our mind.

Before simple organisms had consciousness there was lack of awareness. After the advent of consciousness there was a need for periodic sleep - a return to the earlier simpler state of unconsciousness. So, in a way the temporary regression could be seen as analogous to ordinary sleep. A little like having a nap, a person in ordinary waking consciousness could drift into this temporary atavistic regression experience it for a time and then counter regress (or return) to the normal waking state.

Meares sometimes found that after his best efforts to treat patients some got much better, much more quickly than psychiatric theory at the time said they should. Such patients did so without the critical insight that theory said they must have before they could improve. It seemed to Meares that the improvement was due to the experience of hypnosis rather than the treatments that went with it. He had developed "nonspecific suggestive therapy"[21] in which the hypnotist spoke relatively little making only general suggestions of calm and well being. The hypnotist took on a sense of calm and gently guided the subject. This is in contrast to the authoritarian approach. In that approach the hypnotist induces hypnosis by taking on prestige and authority - commanding the subject - who is then pushed or even jumps into hypnosis. Meares says that he found that 10 sessions of his new method, nonspecific suggestive therapy, often gave his patients a "boost" that helped them to cope much better with their circumstances.

However, Meares found that it was still problematic trying to hypnotise a few subjects using this passive approach. So, a year or two later, began helping such patients to learn this experience of calm for themselves. As he put it, he helped these patients made a transition directly from consciousness to this calm relaxed experience which was under an easy, gentle voluntary control. People are inclined to think of hypnosis as one unvarying state. But it is not. There are several states eg. the waking state, the sleep state, the abreacting or emotional state and so on. The wizard of hypnosis had found yet another state: he referred to it as a yoga like state or Y state.[22]

The first written accounts of hypnosis and meditation date back thousands of years to India, Egypt and Greece. Essentially, in these cultures the skilled priests and priestesses practised meditation themselves and helped the untrained ordinary people through

21 Brit J Med Hypnotism 17(2):16-19. 1956
22 J Clin Exp Hypnosis 8(4): 237-241. 1960

hypnosis (eg. sleep temples etc). Meares had read his way through the vast literature on hypnosis, and later reviewed its history in textbooks[23]. He was fully aware of the accounts of the pain control by yogis and of Europeans who had acquired knowledge of yogic methods and then used this for medical purposes[24]. So, to Meares, the Far East was the obvious place to go find out about the human potential to develop a "healthy" mental ability to inhibit pain[25]. A person with this ability would need little or no drugs and would feel less discomfort. He had in mind helping patients suffering from pain due to incurable cancer, as it was a harrowing experience for both doctor and patient.

So to Asia he went. Firstly, to Burma where he met yogis and then to the New India Institute of Medical Research[26]. He met more yogis there. He also participated in research comparing the brainwaves (EEG) response of a subject to a painful stimulus (hand dipped in ice) when awake and under hypnosis. Hypnosis greatly increased the duration the subject could keep his hand in ice. The experiment had to be cut short due to concerns the subject might sustain a frostbite injury. The brainwaves generated were also compared with brainwave graphs from separate experiments where the subject was in yogic meditation. There were strong similarities between both brainwave graphs taken during the two states of hypnosis and meditation. The conclusion being that the brain states during hypnosis and yogic meditation had a lot in common.

In mid 1960, Meares travelled on to Kathmandu, then a remote area. He wrote that he had heard that he might be able to find yogis still practising traditional methods "unaffected" by civilisation. At Kathmandu, he met with an old yogi. This was Jayanthan Nambudiripad who later took the religious name Govindananda Bharati. Bharati was exceedingly well educated, had travelled widely in Europe and elsewhere and spoke fluent English. Others[27] say that on his travels Bharati met Queen Victoria, Einstein, George Bernard Shaw, Madam Curie, President Roosevelt, Wilhelm Kaiser and Tolstoy amongst others. There are also stories that he visited Mecca, the Vatican and the holy places of other religions. Eventually, Bharati settled on a knoll in Shivpuri (or Shivapuri) forest at the foot of the Himalayas, near Kathmandu, where he became known as the Shivapuri Baba and taught swadharma, the primordial way, also

---

23 Schneck JM (Ed). Hypnosis in Modern Medicine,pp390-405 1963; Medical System of Hypnosis.

24 eg refer James Braid, On Hypnotism. 1860

25 Quarterly J World Fed Mental Health 4(11):158-159. 1959

26 Chhina G, Meares A et al. Indian J Physiol Pharmacol 5(1):43-8, 1961

27 Bennett JG Long Pilgrimage.1965

known as Right Life.

In his discussions and sayings[28] the Baba mentions all the major religions and leading protagonists of them as well as famous people like Newton and Einstein, Shakespeare and Mahatma Gandhi etc. According to the Baba[29] *"Truth is spoken in all the religions. And every religion takes you to the same Goal: For Christianity- 10 Commandments; for Buddhists- Sheel, Samadhi, and Pragyan. For Mohammedan- 5 Noble Truths; for Hindus- Swadharma. These are all Right Life-more or less..." "Religions leads to Right Life and Right Life to God." "Right Life must be lived if one wants to cure himself of the diseases of mortality and misery"*.

Meares says that he asked a guide if there were any local yogis and he was taken to see an old yogi (Shivapuri Baba) who lived in the forest. Later, Meares became aware that this yogi was said to be 134 years old was well educated and had travelled on a pilgrimage. It seems Meares had only basic details about the Baba's full background. He mentions little of it and it was almost certainly never discussed. The old yogi was modest and lived in the moment, not the past.

At his first meeting, Meares[30] asked the old yogi about pain: *"First I asked him... 'Are you ever troubled by pain?' 'No.' 'Do you ever feel pain?' 'Yes. I feel pain.' Then after a pause he added, 'But there is not hurt in it."* At some point the old yogi also said *"Pain is increased 10-fold by anxiety and 100-fold by fear. When we are free from anxiety and fear the pain that is left is not too bad"*[31]. This was far more than Meares hoped to hear.

Meares arrived the same day as another traveller. Hugh Ripman, an Englishman, who was a year or so older than Meares. Ripman's background[32] was banking. He had worked for a London Bank, the War Office and after the war ended he took a senior job with the World Bank. His work took him on periodic trips to distant places. He combined these trips with his own search for spiritual truth seeking out teachers like the Shivapuri Baba. He had visited the Baba 5 years earlier and had come back to visit again. Ripman kept a travel diary![33] and he records meeting an "Australian doctor". The doctor and Ripman had never previously met. Neither was aware of the other's meeting with the Baba that first day. But they met at the old yogi's dwelling on the second day. The doctor arriving a little after Ripman

28 Right Life. Teachings of the Shivapuri Baba. Renu Lal Singh. 1975; Teachings of the Shivapuri Baba. Shrestha, YB. 2000

29 Sayings of the Shivapuri Baba. p4,p11, p13

30 Strange Places and Simple Truths, pp29-58

31 Addition to Meares quote in some of old yogi's students works

32 Oral history interview Ripman, H. World Bank Group Archives. Jul 1961

33 Ripman, H. Search for Truth. Ch. 9, pp121-144, 1999

had done on the second day.

Ripman writes: *"The Australian doctor was very much interested in problems connected with pain and had made much use of hypnotism as a means of relieving pain."*

The doctor stayed half an hour and excused himself, asking whether he might return the following morning. Ripman says the doctor told him later that he did not want to intrude upon Ripman's conversation with the Baba.

After the doctor left, and Ripman was alone with the Baba Ripman writes: *"we sat quietly together... From time to time, however, he... ask, "are you happy?" I was indeed, for, quite apart the peace and quietness of the place..., I was sensitive all the time to the emanation, love and goodness from the presence of the Baba...."*

After visiting the old yogi both Meares and Ripman separately went to view a festival for the goddess Dhurga that was being celebrated that day.

About the festival, Meares writes: *"I was with a friend. During the whole day we saw only one other European"*[34].

Ripman writes *"I was the only European in sight for a long time... After some time, I saw the heads of two other white men,... and realized that one of them was the Australian doctor... The other man was his brother. The doctor explained to me that he was psychiatrist, and a leading exponent in the use of hypnotism both for the relief of pain and for the therapeutic purposes. He was making a trip through these parts of the world in search of people like the Baba, in order to see whether they could throw light on the problems in which he was interested."*

Back at the hotel they conversed and Ripman says that the Australian doctor gave him *"an interesting book he had written to record an experiment in the use of the symbolic painting in healing a mad woman."* Meares wrote **The Door of Serenity** about a schizophrenic woman who brought him paintings which he used to help her eventually heal herself.

The next day Meares and Ripman travelled to meet with the old yogi together. The old yogi had previously told Ripman and Meares that he spent most of the day and night in meditation and hardly slept. But, for the other six hours of his day they could come and sit with him (ie separately or both at the same time).

Meares, Ripman and the Baba held discussions that lapsed into silences. Ripman goes on: *"The doctor asked a question about mesmerism, referring to something said the previous day. "Mesmerism is not good", said the Baba. "Too much force is used. It*

---

34 Strange Places and Simple Truths, pp29-58

is like too much electricity being passed through a wire which is too thin"." Mesmerism is an old term used to describe hypnotism.[35]

The conversation continued with Meares saying: *"I have found... if people learn to meditate on calmness, it helps them with their anxieties".* *"It may do so"*, said the old yogi, *"but meditation on calmness cannot take the place of meditation of God"*...

Meares had been teaching patients the Y state, something he recognised as meditation, before he went to Kathmandu.

Ripman, although extremely reluctant had to leave that day for business reasons. He said his good byes to the Baba and Meares drove him back to where he was staying.

Meares continued to visit the old yogi each day for a total of about 8 days and spent perhaps 50 hours with him in discussion interspersed with silence as he tried to understand and translate the old yogis' thoughts on meditation and swadharma into their western psychological equivalent. Perhaps, that makes it sound a little mundane. It was nothing of the sort.

Meares described his interaction with the old yogi as an encounter.[36] In existentialist and psychological circles an encounter refers to a relationship with profoundly deep understanding and meaning between two persons who do not really know each other at the outset. Meares[37] said *"This man was completely different from any other man I have ever seen. He was serene... I cannot tell you what it was like because I know nothing with which I can compare it... the depths of his serenity would fill me as we talked of life and death, of God and man.*

Meares says as the days passed this experience became more profound - substantially deepening his own sense of calm. Something he said was unexpected (ie *"I had not come for that"*) and that persisted on his return to Australia.

An American colleague of Meares who tried to see the old yogi a year or so later was turned away until he mentioned that the Australian doctor had sent him to visit. Shivpuri Baba died 3 years after Meares met him and today is recognised as a saint by his Hindu countryman in Southern India and Nepal. The Australian doctor[38] is mentioned in various documents written by his students and is regarded as more than just another visitor. Indeed, he is counted by them, like Hugh Ripman and others, as one of the old yogi's special foreign students who left better for their discussions and whose

---

35 after Franz Mesmer, an early hypnotist who used passing movements and believed that "animal magnetism" resulted in the subject being hypnotised.

36 Bower, H ANZ J Psychiatry Vol21(2): 251–252. 1987

37 Strange Places and Simple Truths, pp29-58

38 aka Ainsley\ Ainsue Miers\ Miens\ Maeres\ Mearns.

subsequent work was enhanced and positively influenced as a result.

Before Kathmandu, Meares had been teaching the **Relaxing Mental Exercise** to his patients. The old yogi had practised meditation for longer than many humans live, did not know anxiety or fear and his pain did not hurt. Meeting the embodiment of a lifetime spent in meditation, together with his own profound encounter with this saintly figure, showed Meares the possibilities for himself and his patients.

Kiss Or Curse?

This biography is based on the written works of Ainslie Meares and it would not be complete without at least some reference to his play. **The Kiss of Jocasta** was written before May 1961[39] possibly during or just after his trip to India and Kathmandu.

Jocasta (Homer's Epicasta) was the mother of Oedipus who killed his father (Laius) and then unknowingly married his mother. This was the basis of the naming of the controversial Oedipal complex: several negative 1950s plays\movies portrayed this complex (and related aspects of personality) as fixed and persisting into adulthood; inevitably resulting in the same negative scenario being played out time and time again. These plays and films portrayed characters in modern times being inevitably driven to destructive and often criminal action.

Meares wrote that watching these negative scenarios resulted in the audience leaving the theatre a little worse for it. In reply, as it were, in his play, characters interact, are challenged, rise above the difficulties, find positive solutions and become better people as a result - Jocasta's kiss is merely a kiss rather than a curse – the audience is uplifted and as Meares put it "*and the high purpose of dramatic art is fulfilled*".

It seems Meares provided copies to various people to illustrate the psychological benefits of good theatre. To help them understand that childhood conflicts need not be inevitably and repeatedly played out in adult life. That people are capable of great change as they grow and mature. Something he went on to repeat again and again in various later publications. Also, hidden within the play is Meares expression that his work was leading him in a new direction.

---

39 Copyright application dated 11 May 1961

1.3 Relief Without Drugs (RWD) Period

Regression

His trip to India and his encounter with the saintly old yogi all acted as a catalyst for Meares to all but abandon "classical" hypnosis and shift his focus towards atavistic regression. He wrote papers published in the Lancet in 1961: *What makes the patient better?*[40] and followed this up in 1962 with his reply *Atavistic regression as a basic factor*[41]. In other words, it was the temporary regression and profound calm that came with it that was important. Further, this temporary regression was essentially a natural process that periodically, spontaneously occurred in the minds of normal people to reduce anxiety.

To quote his Lancet paper: *"In ordinary health there are continual variations in the level of our mental alertness. For a while we function in a completely rational fashion with our criticism alert to every step in our thinking. Then the intensity of our critical functioning wanes, and our awareness of reasoned logic becomes less acute. The process may go a step further and we find ourselves quite off guard, in a momentary state of reverie...*

These normal variations in the level of mental functioning can be explained more easily as a temporary slipping back to a more primitive mode of functioning....the important point is that persons suffering from chronic anxiety do not experience the same fluctuations in the level of mental functioning. They are continually alert and on guard, with their critical faculties constantly working at high pressure. This idea is expressed in the phrase we hear so often "I simply can't relax"...

What is the significance of this strange loss of the normal variations in the level of mental functioning? Could it be that these periods of atavistic regression are somehow necessary for the homeostatic mechanisms of the mind to function effectively? In this respect we have a clear analogy to our recurrent need for sleep."

Over several decades, Meares referred to the experience of the calm of atavistic regression as auto-hypnosis, pure hypnosis, meditative experience, the Relaxing Mental Exercise, mental ataraxis, intensive meditation and other terms mentioned in this biography. Today, it is referred to as Stillness Meditation or Stillness Meditation Therapy (SMT®).

Both hypnosis and Stillness Meditation involve the temporary

---

40 Lancet (7189):1280-1. 1961
41 Lancet (7221):151-3. 1962

regression to the simpler state of mind. Stillness Meditation involves the "pure" regression - it could be said to be hypnosis but without the "phenomena of hypnosis"[42] including the absence of the figure of the hypnotist. The regressed person in Stillness Meditation, experiences the regression and relaxation, and gently retains control of themselves although there is a sense of letting go.

Subjects in "conventional" hypnosis undergo this temporary regression via learning from the hypnotist and may exhibit various phenomena including amnesia, catalepsy, rigidities, hallucinations - all abnormal states of mind. This contrasts clearly with "pure" hypnosis (ie. the regressive state without phenomena), which is essentially a normal state. A state experienced from time to time by all normal people in moments of reverie and mental relaxation where there is spontaneous temporary regression to more primitive functioning (under voluntary control and without phenomena!).

Meares eventually came to believe that the phenomena of hypnosis were recognised by the subject as odd. Subjects knew of hypnotic phenomena from the theatre and the subjects made to experience the phenomena felt cheapened by the therapist. For example, being hypnotised by being commanded to be unable to move an arm that becomes rigid. None of this oddness or cheapening is present in the experience of "pure" hypnosis.

Meares had found that the results obtained by just using relaxation and regression (without phenomena etc) far surpassed those previously obtained by the various earlier methods he had researched, developed and improved. The result was that he completely re-wrote **System of Medical Hypnosis**. His new book **The Management of the Anxious Patient** was published in 1963. By 1967, he had re-written **"Management"** as a self help book for the general population. The new book was entitled **Relief without Drugs (RWD)**. It was a major hit and has since been translated into at least a dozen different languages and there is an audio version. A distillation of **RWD** published later forms Section 2 of this book.

Pain And Discomfort

On his expeditions to the Far East to find out about the potential to develop a "healthy" ability to inhibit pain[43] Meares met the Shivapuri Baba who lived near Kathmandu. Aside from witnessing the outcome of a lifetime of serenity and sharing in it during his encounter with the Baba, a major learning was the old yogi's

---

42 Int J Clin Exp Hypnosis16(4): 211–214. 1968
43 Quarterly J World Fed Mental Health 4(11):158-159. 1959

242

242

N3   Row 17   Bay 17

3IIK10005Z2B

Title	AINSLIE MEARES ON MEDITATION:
Condition	Good
Description	Signs of wear and consistent use.
Source	ALB
ASIN	0646966936
Code	9780646966939
Catalog	Book
Employee	ecim-rs
Listed	4/12/2022 9:25:11 AM
Tags	

Thank you for your purchase.

statement that he felt pain but it did not hurt. Meares says[44] *"First I asked him about pain, as this was the problem which was uppermost in my mind. 'Are you ever troubled by pain?' 'No.' 'Do you ever feel pain?' 'Yes. I feel pain.' Then after a pause he added, 'But there is not hurt in it.'"* *"These few words were to have quite a profound effect on my professional career and my life in general."*

Ripman recalls another conversation the following day. *"The Australian doctor .... had made much use of hypnotism as a means of relieving pain. He asked SB about this. "Pain is inevitable", he said, "If you know the cause of the pain, then you can bring relief by medicine. Otherwise, you have to learn to bear it. Pain and pleasure, heat and cold, these are things that come and go". He paused, and looked at the doctor. "The trouble is that you dislike pain. You need to learn not to dislike it".* Not masochism but pain experienced merely as a sensation – a warning signal that does not hurt.

In 1961, Meares travelled to Bali and witnessed a fire dance where the dancer walked the coals apparently without pain. On questioning the participants he learnt that the dancer was not specially trained but was just one of the villagers who participated in a brief ceremony prior to the dance. This led him to conclude that the process of learning pain control might be simpler than he had thought[45]. That no lengthy special training was required ie. one did not have to be an advanced yogi to learn pain control. Since the late 1950s, Meares had believed that the mind could inhibit pain and had self experimented since then. It seems likely that it was then that Meares began to experiment further upon himself to learn the complete experience of pain without hurt. In late 1962, an opportunity came when one of his teeth had to be extracted. He decided that this was an ideal test. So he asked a dentist he knew if he would take the tooth out without any injection. At first the dentist refused but after several days finally agreed. So, on 19 December 1962[46], Meares relaxed, as he put it, in the way of the old yogi of Kathmandu, and the dentist extracted the tooth without discomfort, for the patient, anyway! The dentist was astounded. He told Meares that he had had to cut the gum and peel it off the bone, then chisel away the bone and remove the tooth sideways. Meares said that this first extraction, gave him renewed confidence in continuing to develop his methods. Some 15 years later, Meares[47] recounted that he had had one cyst excised from his neck and 4 teeth extracted without medication and without discomfort.

---

44 Strange Places and Simple Truths, pp 29-58
45 Annals Aust College Dent Surg. 1:42-6. 1967
46 Med J Aust Jun p820. 1963
47 The Wealth Within, p56

The inhibition of pain was not the only learning from Meares' expedition. Around 1960, he wrote: *"some minor degree of physical discomfort such as lying on a hard, uncomfortable surface seems to aid the process. The patient... transcends feelings of comfort or discomfort".*[48] In 1961, after his trip to India and Kathmandu, discomfort was[49] *"a necessary part in the attainment of the meditative state. It has the effect of preventing the meditating yogi from falling asleep. This again has its counterpart in clinical hypnosis, in which the patient is able to attain a greater depth of hypnosis if he is not too comfortable, and is less likely to escape from hypnotic sleep into natural sleep."*

The meditation posture must provide minor discomfort.

Too little postural discomfort – being too comfortable - resulted in a pleasant drowsiness that the nerves in the limbs and torso report to the brain. This has little effect in lowering the level of anxiety. The relaxation wanted comes from the mind as it transcends minor discomfort. One relaxes if it is easy to transcend the discomfort. Too much discomfort results in tensing and trying to endure. This is not what was wanted.

Later, Meares' extended discomfort from posture to include its cousins: variety, distraction and disturbance. These stimuli are also discussed later in the book.

Spreading The Word

RWD increased Meares' audience enormously but he continued to search for more efficient approaches to communicate his method. His novel **Where Magic Lies** is parable like and in the preface he says "...*This is the magic. If just a little of it should come to you as you read, I shall be well rewarded".* Beatle mania focussed the attention of the West on yoga months before he wrote an article titled "Umm"[50]. Umm was non-verbal phonation – a communicative sound - that Meares used as one of his channels of communication with patients[51]. To his patients it was a communication of ease and satisfaction. In relation to the article, Umm was a play on words. Depending on how you said it, Umm could also be used to express disbelief or enjoyment[52]. Also, it could sound a bit like a yogic mantra word (eg. "Om"). Yoga and Om were all the rage. The Umm article, outlined how the "big doctors" might communicate calm and ease to patients using "Umm" language, *"the true language of long ago when*

---

48 Medical System of Hypnosis, Chapter 41, pp358-363
49 Meares 3rd World Congress Psychiatry. Montreal. V1:712-714, 1961
50 Med J Aust p688. 1968
51 Lancet 275(7126): 663–667. 1960
52 A Better Life, p24

we were primitive and things were simple." The article ends: *"during the process of evolution the functions of mind have progressed from relative simplicity to greater and greater complexity. In atavistic regression our mind returns to the simple and more primitive mode of functioning. By non-verbal communication, atavistic regression can be induced to allay anxiety and reduce the patient's general level of tension."*

Interest in the mysticism of the Far East continued to explode and Meares responded by writing about the **Strange Places and Simple Truths** of his travels and interactions with yogis, mystics, and so on whom practised altered states of consciousness. The tales are engaging but the message is encouragement to learn relaxation and regression.

Meares expressed a high level of regard for genuine yogis and other mystics but was always adamant that his method was not Yoga per se, Buddhism or anything else.

After Yoga became popular in the West, he constructively emphasised the differences between his method and Zen, Yoga etc. He also believed that there were common elements of temporary regression present in some, but not all, Yoga and Zen practices[53][54]. The idea of atavistic regression upset some yogis and Zen practitioners who misunderstood. They thought they were achieving higher, nobler states. Meares seemed to be telling them that they were becoming primitive barbarians! This was not what he meant. Rather, simpler can mean better. A temporary going back to simple can erase the errors of complexity and the flawless foundations can permit growth far higher and nobler than before.

Essentially one might say that it was Meares' view that his instructions and approach were clearer, simpler, more direct and efficient, although, not everyone found them easy to understand. However, if it were easy, then there would be no need for instructions or teachers as everyone would just be doing it. The crux of the problem was that it was easier to show people with a genuine interest than to explain his method.

Groups [55][56]

Before Eastern meditation became popular Meares had described his method as Relaxing Mental Exercise or auto-hypnosis. Telling the relatives that the patient had to practice Relaxing Mental Exercise or "auto-hypnosis" at home could sometimes be problematic.

53 Third World Congress Psychiatry Vol 1 pp712-714 1961
54 Existential Psychiatry Summer-Fall 1969 pp119-121
55 Med J Aust 13(9):675-6. 1971; Med J Aust 15(4):733-4. 1973
56 Hypnosis in the Seventies. (Ed) LE Uneståhl. pp110-112. 1975

The relatives might not understand what they had not experienced first-hand for themselves. The patient might feel uncomfortable or embarrassed about the "special" exercise etc. To avoid this situation, Meares found it useful to involve the husband and wife, or the parent and the child, in the exercise, so that the relatives would understand what the patient was doing. The parent could then practice with the child; the couple could practice together; or the patient could practice by themselves and the relatives would at least understand what it was about and keep out of the way etc. Duos and trios led to larger groups.

Clearly, one person facilitating the Relaxing Mental Exercise for a group of several people was more efficient. There is an old saying about "taking on the mood of the crowd" which often refers to an individual taking on the mood of a fearful, tense group merely by being present in that group. There also exists a similar phenomenon where people take on the "calm of the crowd".

In primitive times, if danger was detected by one in the tribe others also sensed it. This enhanced a quicker response and increased the likelihood of survival of the group. Conversely, if there was no danger then the peace felt by the group enhanced the restoration of body and mind and helped to bind the group together. This also had survival value.

Anyone who has practised the Meares method individually and also in groups will be aware of this phenomenon though direct experience. Meares was certainly aware of the person to person communication of calm having made use of it himself since the mid 1950s, experienced the effect in Kathmandu and writing in the Lancet[57] of the analogies between the doctor and the patient and how *"in much the same way as those who come for help take on the serenity of a yogi or guru in the east"*. This was in the context that meditating on calm cured asthma.

Meares would have received abundant positive feedback from participants in such groups. Group sessions allowed the participants a deeper experience of calm and meant several people were taught at once rather than one by one. It was perhaps around 1968 that Meares began to run group sessions for his patients in a ten seat room – the first Quiet Place. He had treated around 1,000 patients in it by 1971.

That same year while trying to explain his ideas to an audience of psychiatrists and psychologists, he abandoned the explanation and instead provided an impromptu demonstration of his group method. This was extremely well received. Over the next few days he gave demonstrations for groups of 50-60 people several times. Through the 1970s and into the early 1980s, Meares continued to present

57 Lancet p1380, 1963

group sessions at professional seminars and conferences in Australia and overseas.

In early 1972 an advertisement began to appear in the Melbourne "Age" Newspaper which stated: A meeting to experience and learn the art of MENTAL RELAXATION to help people with a minor degree of NERVOUS TENSION will be held in Melbourne on [date] at [time]. The meeting is sponsored and conducted by an experienced medical practitioner who for professional reasons wishes to remain anonymous. No fee. No collection. Not religious.

The advertisement went on to outline how to respond.

In August 1972, a journalist who worked for the paper that carried the adverts attended one of these free sessions. The journalist told Meares that he knew his name and planned to expose him. Meares told the journalist that he ran free public sessions as a community service to those who could not afford to pay to see him as a patient. Meares explained that he had paid for everything but did tell people attending that they should read **Relief Without Drugs** to understand the theory a little better. He said that his royalties were less than two cents a copy or a total of less than a dollar per group which was a loss considering he paid for the advertisement, rented the hall and all other costs etc. The Melbourne Age Newspaper reported[58] the group sessions were meditative self-hypnosis. Meares described his work with large groups using various combinations of the following terms: group relaxing auto-hypnotic meditative experience. There was no one name. Rather, he seems to have used various descriptions to attract that audience to his method.

Despite Meares' community service being anonymous and resulting in a monetary loss the exposure by the "Age" caused friction with the medical associations. Meares continued to teach groups of up to sixty people at a time who had responded to his advertisement for several years. The sixty seat room in which this occurred eventually became known as the Quiet Place. Eventually, in the late 1970s he abandoned the free sessions as the persons who were attending were academics and professionals who could well afford to pay and the places they took up were at the expense of his target audience.

---

58 The Age. 15 August 1972. p2

1.4 Stillness Meditation Period

Positive Psychiatry

Meares had applied his method to the most urgent matters, the replacement of anxiety with calm and pain by pain without hurt. In 1958, he had seen "the distant horizon".[59] which he described at the end of **Relief without Drugs** as the "fringe benefits". He now began to help people, as he put it, who would generally not be regarded as mentally unwell and would never normally see a psychiatrist.

He said[60] *"I speak as a doctor... I am concerned with the individual's physical health and his psychological health, but I am also concerned with his spiritual health, because without this, the other two can never be complete."*

He believed that there was great potential for helping a great many people to live a better life. What we might call positive psychiatry – akin to the much later "positive psychology" movement. Meares wrote about various aspects of his new understanding for different audiences.

Many years earlier, Meares had written about **Marriage and Personality** and **The Introvert**.

This was around the time of the hippy movement and the Vietnam War protests. Meares spoke out on what he regarded as the causes and solutions for the unrest and striving of youth. He wrote two books for youth and their parents - **Student Problems and a Guide to Study** and his **Dialogue with Youth**. The latter book analyses the phenomenon of youth – the period between adolescence and adult life which had been extended by education. It discusses positive and negative reactions of youth including the reactions which lead some young people to drop out, take drugs or show other symptoms of alienation.

The late 1960s-1970s were at the time of the widespread rise of the women's liberation movement and feminism. This was a time of significant social change. **The New Woman** was not only about the new feminist woman but also her traditional sister - women at the crossroads of social and psychological evolution. It was written for feminist and traditional women as well as men seeking to understand the changes that were occurring. Around the time the book was released a television program[61] organised by the Women's Electoral Lobby (WEL) was aired in which a panel consisting of Delys Sargeant,

---

59 Med J Aust 45(26):857-8, 1958
60 Student Problems & A Guide to Study, p17
61 Several Personal Communications from WEL affiliated persons.

Beatrice Faust and Meares discussed women and feminism in front of a live audience. The title of Meares talk was: "Sex roles - natural or learnt". Although, Meares was sometimes misunderstood by some he was a supporter of feminism: *"I wholeheartedly support the aims and aspirations of the women's liberation movement[62]"*.

For the worker and his\her boss he wrote about quality of life in **The Way Up** and **How to be a Boss**. As far as can be seen these two books are virtually identical. However, the themes of these books were really about are communication, quality of life and the psychological reactions in coping with people. By this time he was well known and a public figure. For example,[63] he spoke on Radio and was reported in Newspapers about **The Way Up** which sold for 95c.

In **Why be Old?** Meares shows how most of the characteristics of ageing are due to psychological over-compensation rather than the ageing process itself. This can be relieved in the aged and largely avoided by the young as they grow into and through middle age.

He wrote **Lets be Human** about the psychological and sociological evolution of humanity. It was a more general discussion of his positive psychiatric philosophy on which the earlier books (eg **The Way Up, Dialogue with Youth, The New Woman, Why be Old**) are based. It was about how we are all participating in the process of psychological evolution. Old and outworn patterns of reaction are being abandoned and new emergent ones are evolving. These new capacities can transcend the constriction of logic and bring understanding to mystical and spiritual experience.

After the controversial dismissal of an Australian Prime Minister he seized the opportunity to write about **The Hidden Powers of Leadership**. In a way, the book was an extension of aspects of **Lets be Human** in that it concerned how politicians and other leaders might influence us as individuals but also how we as individuals with leadership roles might influence others for better or for worse. At the time **Hidden Powers** was written Meares was experiencing conflict from some parts of the medical profession regarding his cancer work. **Hidden Powers** may contain some of Meares constructive pondering to fully understand what underlay the conflict as well as how he might best and most constructively move forwards.

The Wealth Within was a follow on book written 10 years after **Relief without Drugs (RWD).** It includes his experience since **RWD** and emphasises the "fringe benefits" and the flowing on through life of the calm experienced in Stillness Meditation. By "fringe benefits" he meant a better quality of life experienced at work,

62 The Hidden Powers of Leadership, p55.
63 Canberra Times, 29 April 1972, p13 & 29 May 1972, p7

at leisure, in the home, and in personal and romantic relationships.

The elusive "flow" of positive psychology was to be sought out by engaging in activities in the hope of finding it[64]. The process of flowing or moving steadily onward Meares referred to as onflow. Meares' onflow of mental calm and bodily ease arising from meditation seeped through the person's life. Living calm[65] is the aim of Stillness Meditation. Meares strongly believed in Stillness Meditation to live a better life; rather than living to merely meditate. Dropping out or becoming a recluse might reduce anxiety but would also involve missing out.

The medical profession already had ataractic drugs – drugs which calmed the patient down. In the mid 1970s, Meares coined a new term from the Greek, mental ataraxis i.e. a state of unperturbed mental tranquillity. The new name was largely to distinguish mental ataraxis from transcendental meditation and other forms as his method was far simpler, had no initiating ceremony, no mantra and involved meditation in slight discomfort (rather than comfort)[66].

Several years later, he stopped using the term (mental ataraxis) as he found it confused some people. Instead, referring to his method as intensive meditation. From the 1970 onwards he often used the term stillness, wrote of the mind becoming still and of stilling the mind. In the mid 1980s he described his meditation *"as no striving, no mental activity, just quietness, a stillness of effortless tranquillity. This is not the tranquillity of drowsy sleepiness. The mind is clear but still."*[67]

Speaking in 1981, about the state of consciousness during Stillness Meditation, Meares succinctly said *"Awake. Not asleep. Not unconscious. Clear. Not drowsy. But, the mind is in fact still"* [68]

Meares had raised concerns with his colleagues about the over-use of potions to control pain and anxiety since the late 1950s[69]. In 1971[70] Meares appeared before a House of Representatives Select Committee into the pharmaceutical benefit scheme in operation then. He raised concerns regarding the over usage of anti-depressant drugs. He said that it was not that the drugs or drug houses are wrong, it is the way the drugs were prescribed. This was in addition to his public advertisements for free group sessions. The medical associations were unhappy with what they felt was blatant advertising.

---

64 Csikszentmihalyi, M. Flow: The psychology of optimal experience. 1990
65 Living Calm in a Busy World - Title of Pauline McKinnon's book
66 Aust Fam Physician 5(7): 906-10. 1976
67 Life without Stress
68 The Healing Power of Meditation, 14\7\81, Qld Relaxation Centre (CD)
69 Quarterly J World Fed Mental Health 4(11):158-159, 1959
70 6 February 1971

In any event, in 1973 Meares had *"retired from medical practice in order to gain freedom of expression of his own views about mental relaxation, and to specialize as a non-medical consultant helping people though relaxing meditative experience"*[71].

He was never de-registered as has been incorrectly been hinted at. He chose to remove what he felt was becoming a restraint on his work. Freed of that restraint he moved to work on a new frontier.

Cancer

Since his early work Meares had been aware that disease processes of the body and mind were not separate. Rather, all diseases included both a physical and a mental component which might vary in individual cases. Patterns tended to be present for particular diseases. Patients he had treated for various conditions, as early as 1950, reported to him an unexpected bonus, their asthma had gone or was much improved. The allergic response is an immune response. An aberrant immune response is involved in cancer formation and Meares says this led him to wonder if treating the mind might also affect cancer[72].

Before his trip to India, some 10 years later, he was seeing cancer patients in pain. They were part of the reason he went to India[73]. His learning and teaching of pain without hurt would only have increased the number of cancer patients he saw. Meares must have seen the growth of cancer slowed and held back in some lucky patients. But, he put off following up this observation[74]. Now, he had already written down do-it-yourself instructions in **RWD**, developed his group facilitation method and written several books about his positive philosophy. At that time, society was "cancer-phobic" and focussed on external causes (eg. asbestos, pesticides, UV). The incidence of cancer appeared to be on the increase with roughly 1 in every 4 deaths due to cancer back then. Meares knew the idea that the mind might contribute to cancer or cure it would be controversial. He was no stranger to controversy which had been an inevitable side effect of his past ground breaking work. Cancer must have seemed like the next, greatest and perhaps the last frontier. Having resigned from medical registration (he retained membership with various medical associations) there was nothing to stop him.

He pushed on ahead and responsibly advertised, as a non-medical consultant on meditation and hypnosis, for the sickest, nearly

---

71 Aust Family Physician 3(May):164, 1974
72 A Way of Doctoring, p113
73 A Better Life, p113
74 The Silver Years, p210

dead cancer patients he could find[75] and saw them without charge saying that meditation would help with better coping and pain control. He advised them that these were side effects as his research was really about whether or not meditation might affect the growth of cancer. In addition, he advised that they should realise that the odds of overcoming the cancer were extremely minute. One by one he wrote up case reports[76] showing patients who had retarded the growth of cancer.

Over time as the numbers of patients grew, he reported:[77] *"roughly 10% have clear evidence of regression of the cancer in the absence of orthodox treatment which could cause the cancer to regress. Another 10% have shown marked slowing of the growth, and a further 10% a less marked but still significant slowing in the rate of growth"... ..90% of all the patients reported much less pain and less need of pain killing drugs."*

Nearly all his patients who kept up with meditation reported:

- improved coping ie *"greater ease of mind, less anxiety and depression and sleep better"* and
- that they were far better equipped to be able to die with dignity if it should come to that.

After Meares' case reports on cancer patients began to appear he started to use the term intensive meditation[78]. This reflected the long duration and particularly emphasised the depth of the meditation. These long periods, hours per day, being needed to influence physiology – so as to create a physiological regression. A re-calibration, if you like, of the body's nervous and endocrine systems. This recalibration removed the old, incorrect response and replaced it with the correct pattern. Even though the meditation was for long periods Meares observed that those who did best were the ones who had been able to integrate the onwards flow of calm into their own lives. The effects of meditation flow steadily onwards for a period after the meditation session has finished. During this time the meditator experiences a sense of calm. Those who learned to encourage this flow on so as to live calm, did best.

Humans are naturally inclined to want to improve what they learn. The easiest way to do this is to add to it. To make it more. But, more is not better. More is more. More may be complicated and less efficient.

---

75 Med J Aust Jun & Oct 1975

76 Ref's listed in A Way of Doctoring, p151-152 & A Better Life, p148-149

77 J Helen Vale Found V3(2):13-16. 1982; Aust Fam Physician 9(May):322-325 ; Also The Silver Years p81-84

78 Amer Soc Psychosom Dent & Med. J 25(4): 129-132. 1978

Simple can also be subtle. Just as going back to a simpler function, to sound foundations, can permit growth to a higher level, the reverse, complexity, can mean stasis. Complexity can bog down the practitioner in prescriptive detail and the outcome can be lost. It can become an elusive mirage that appears tantalisingly in the distance never to be approached or directly experienced. The mirage can also become a set of poor instructions or even dogma.

At one point, when Meares had gone away on a trip, one of his cancer patients sought to "improve" Stillness Meditation. She rapidly deteriorated after she began trying to vividly visualise her immune cells fighting off her cancer[79]. When Meares became aware of the situation he showed her stillness again and her health soon improved.

Decades earlier Meares had explored the subtleties of hypnosis[80] and had also used visualisation[81] back then. His pondering had led him to develop a new theory of hypnosis and this had led to the atavistic regression theory of mental homeostasis. Now he turned his attention to the mental states resulting from different types of meditation. He categorised these as[82]:

1&2 Examining\Contemplative- the mind contemplates or examines some object or idea. The will and intellect are active.

3. Sensory– sensation is active.

4. Emotional - emotion is active with little sensation and thought.

5. Wandering - the mind flits from subject to subject. Intellect is active.

6. Stillness–little or no thought, little or no sensation, no emotion. A simple state of mind where anxiety cannot exist.

Meares concluded that the reduction in anxiety and regression of physiological function were two key factors resulting in intensive meditation retarding the growth of cancer. Further, these other types of meditation may produce some mild reduction in anxiety but cannot produce a regression of physiological functioning as a direct outcome of following their instructions.

Mental ataraxis (stillness) is the outcome of an atavistic regression to a very simple mode of functioning. There is little or no thought, an absence of sensory experience and no emotion. Stillness involves the experience of a simpler state of mind. This simpler state of mind is one in which anxiety cannot exist! Anxiety that remains at a low level for some time after meditation has ceased. A flow on

79 Amer Soc Psychom Dent & Med 25(3): 85-88 1978
80 In Kline, MV (Ed) Psychodynamics and Hypnosis. Ch4, pp32-40, 1967
81 Medical System of Hypnosis. eg. p212, p280
82J Amer Soc Psychom Dent & Med 25(4)129-132 1978

("onflow") of a low level of anxiety into the patient's daily life. As a result this simpler state of mind permits new and better patterns of functioning to emerge.

Meares disapproved of adding unneeded practices that he saw complicated his method. He had researched, developed and fine tuned his method,at that point, for decades. All the unnecessary had been discarded and there was only the pure essence left.

In recent times, others have categorised meditation as focussed attention (examining, contemplative, sensory and emotional) or open monitoring (wandering). Stillness or equivalent is not mentioned. This lack of recognition or lack of awareness of Meares' meditation categories, like much of Meares' work, means that they have never been fully explored and widely discussed.

Koans – Therapeutic Poetry

In 1949, Meares published **How Distant the Stars.** It was his first (known) published work and it was poetry.

"This slim volume contains 11 poems. Five... expound the emotions of those suffering from mental illness... The rest are in rather lighter and happier vein, depicting the jungle...in New Guinea during the war."[83]

The truth of the flow on of the effects of meditation cannot be said. But it can be shown like a finger pointing at the stars. If you look at the finger then you miss the heavenly glory. Now in the mid 1970s, Meares begun to write poems in imitation of the poem riddles (koans) of Zen writing. Meares does not say what brought him to start writing therapeutic poetry for his patients. Perhaps he saw an analogy between the long duration of meditation for cancer and the twin Zen practices of prolonged meditation and pondering koans. Or perhaps in recalling certain effective conversations with patients he recognised he was talking in koan like language. At this time he was thinking about Zen in relation to his philosophy of positive psychiatry[84]. Years later, he states that he wrote *in imitation of Zen writing*[85] [86]"

From the Quiet Place and **Dialogue on Meditation** were simply about meditation. The next poetry books, with some overlap of themes, were **A Kind of Believing, Thoughts** and **Prayer and Beyond** which are about understanding and the spirit.

Meares' wife Bonnie died in 1979. He said that they were extraordinarily close and that when she died he felt in a way that he

---

83 The Advertiser Adelaide 8 Apr 1950, p6
84 Lets be Human eg p171-173
85 Amer J Clin Hyp 25(2-3):114-121. 1983
86 Healing Power of Meditation,1981, Queensland Relaxation Centre (CD).

had too[87]. It is understatement to say it, but this makes some of the poems written around that time particularly poignant.

My Soul and I was a set of personal poems about Meares himself.

Cancer: Another Way? and **A Way of Doctoring** were written for people learning meditation to help heal disease such as cancer, to cope better with pain and the possibility of an approaching death. These books were written specifically for such people and others reading them might find some of the poems uncomfortable. Meares continued to write koan poetry for the rest of his life including the books **Lets be at Ease** and **Man and Woman** both of which were published after his death.

The Silver Years, also published after his death, has many sections accompanied by a poem specifically written around the theme(s) of that section. **A Way of Doctoring** is a sort of poetic version of **RWD** or **Life without Stress. Life without Stress** and **A Better Life** are also tinged with Meares' poetic approach.

Clearly, Meares judged his initial efforts at therapeutic poetry a success as the first book **From the Quiet Place** was followed by many more. Indeed, a substantial portion of Meares' writings from then on was poetry.

Writing It Down

Meares work on cancer added to his fame. From the late 1970s and into the 1980s readers of the "Age" Newspaper could order poetry books written by this "well known psychiatrist" as Christmas gifts. There were further radio, television and newspaper interviews. In 1980, Lily Brett, a journalist who later became an author, wrote about Meares in POL magazine[88]. The name POL stood for nothing but to be in POL was recognition of popularity. Meares was described by Ms Brett as being a combination of Maverick and Edwardian gentleman. She began work on a biography but the project was archived[89]. A biography by Desmond Zwar **Doctor Ahead Of His Time**[90] was completed some years later, in 1985. Meares was the focal point in a TV program[91] aired in late 1983 which also featured one of his cancer patients of whom Meares had written in 1978[92]: *"he developed a degree of calm about him which I have rarely observed... [he] has let the effects of the intense... meditation enter into his whole experience*

---

87 Brett, L (1980) The Maverick Dr Meares. POL Magazine, Feb pp52-57
88 Brett, L (1980) The Maverick Dr Meares. POL Magazine, Feb pp52-57
89 Papers of Lily Brett, ADF Academy Library.
90 aka The Doctor Who Forever Changed the Way We Look at Cancer
91 Healers, Quacks or Mystics, Ep.4. Nevill Drury. 1983
92 Med J Aust. 1978 Oct 21;2(9):433

of life." Writing years later *"It is there in his face for all to see... And now to give to others something of this...* [he] *established a cancer support group[93]"* Ian Gawler learned directly from Meares for several months and left to continue his spiritual quest studying with a range of other meditation and esoteric teachers. He now teaches within a Buddhist like framework, contemplative, examining, sensory, emotional, wandering and stillness meditation.[94]

Pauline McKinnon first met Meares around 1974. In 1983, the publishers of her book **In Stillness Conquer Fear** suggested that she include information on Yoga etc to go with the meditation theme. She reluctantly mentioned this to Meares who had already agreed to write a Foreword to the book. Meares bluntly said that if Yoga were mentioned there would be no forward as it was his method and the two should not be confused. The publisher dropped the Yoga idea and Meares wrote that Foreword. He also wrote about Pauline McKinnon (and her book) in one of his own[95].

Biographies, radio and television had highlighted the work on cancer but more importantly some medical specialists[96] including some from the medical hypnotism community began to acknowledge Meares work on cancer. However, Meares repeatedly said that his work would not be fully appreciated in his own lifetime.

Meares continued to see patients and wrote articles to a wide range of audiences in Australia and overseas. This included both mainstream publications, professional groups and the leading edge fringe. In fact, any audience he believed would learn from his message.

Meares repeatedly told various people that he had not trained anyone specifically to replace him but he had written it all down. Over his career, he had done this in abundance eventually writing a total of 34 books and well over 100 technical publications between 1949 and his unexpected death in late 1986 after he was hospitalised with pneumonia. In the prestigious medical journal, The Lancet[97], he had written publications on hypnosis, communication, diagnosis of pre-psychotic schizophrenia, atavistic regression and cancer. There are many who would be happy to get one article published in the Lancet.

93 A Way of Doctoring, p143

94 Gawler I & Bedson P Meditation An In-depth Guide. 2010

95 A Way of Doctoring, poem 112, p100-101

96 Meares, Horrobin, Ghayur, Karmali Lancet 313(8123): p978. 1979; Sydney Morning Herald 17-3-1985. also, see Desmond Zwar's book.

97 The Lancet 264.6838 (1954): 592-594 & 264.6844(1954) p921, The Lancet 275.7126 (1960): 663-667, The Lancet 273.7063 (1959): 55-58, The Lancet 277.7189 (1961): 1280-1281 & 279.7221 (1962): 151-153 & 281.7295(1963): 1380–1381; The Lancet 313.8123 (1979): 978 & 318.8254 (1981): 1037-1038

Some of Meares best selling books have been translated into 12 languages including Chinese, Dutch, English, French, German, Italian, Korean, Japanese, Russian, Spanish, Swedish and are available as audio and in Braille.

Towards the end of his life, Meares held a meeting with several people who had learnt and were teaching his method[98]. It seemed that Meares thoughts had finally turned to teacher training. He had recently completed a draft of **A Better Life** which, in part, discusses teaching Stillness Meditation. So, the meeting was a preliminary discussion and about how best to launch the new book. His unexpected demise means that whatever he intended did not occur.

After his death, in the years that followed, his Estate published his last 5 books: **Life Without Stress, A Better Life, Lets be at Ease, Man and Woman** and **The Silver Years.** Thus ensuring that what had been written down could be read. Without this work, these books would not have existed. The Estate increased the size of the pool of Meares' books in circulation and published a trilogy of his first 3 poetry books simply entitled **Dialogue on Meditation - From the Quiet Place - A Kind of Believing.**

In 2016, those in Australia trying to find someone to learn Meares' Method from are fortunate to have the Stillness Meditation Therapy Centre and affiliated Meares' Stillness Meditation Teachers. The simple truth is that Pauline McKinnon has carried Meares' torch onward and has implemented a teacher training course – something Ainslie Meares was not able to do during his lifetime.

Acknowledgements

Zwar's and McKinnon's books, the obituary by Bower[99] and private communications support various points in this biography.

---

98 McKinnon P, Living Calm in a Busy World, p196
99 Bower, H. ANZ J Psychiatry Vol21(2): 251–252. 1987

1.5 Ainslie Meares' Books

Poetry Book	*
Rare or Unavailable in 2017	~~Strike through~~
Editors' Picks	**Bold**

Hypnosis Period

*~~How Distant the Stars 1949~~ (150 copies printed; 16 known).
The Medical Interview 1957.
Hypnography 1957.
Marriage and Personality 1957.
The Introvert 1958.
The Door of Serenity 1958.
Shapes of Sanity 1960.
A System of Medical Hypnosis 1960.
~~The Kiss of Jocasta 1961~~ (privately printed; few surviving copies).
For technical readers, **System of Medical Hypnosis** incorporates much of **The Medical Interview.** Unless hypnosis is of special interest pick **Management of the Anxious Patient**.

Meditation Period

The Management of the Anxious Patient 1963 (hard to get).
Relief Without Drugs 1967
Where Magic Lies 1968 (novel)
~~Student Problems & a Guide to Study 1969.~~
Strange Places and Simple Truths 1969 (travels).
The Way Up 1970 \\ How to be a Boss 1971.
Dialogue with Youth 1973.
The New Woman 1974.
Why be Old? 1975 (Silver Years is more recent).
Lets Be Human 1976.
*From the Quiet Place 1976. (60 poems)
The Wealth Within 1978.
~~The Hidden Powers of Leadership 1978.~~
*Cancer: Another Way? 1977. (125 poems)
*Dialogue on Meditation 1979. (96 poems)
*Thoughts 1980. (60 poems)
*Prayer and Beyond 1981. (60 poems)
*~~My Soul and I 1982. (poems)~~
*A Kind of Believing 1984. (52 poems)
***A Way of Doctoring** 1985. (170 poems)
Life Without Stress 1987 (hard to get).
*~~Let's be at Ease. 1987.~~ (60 poems)
*~~Man and Woman 1987.~~ (102 poems)
The Silver Years. 1988 (also includes 32 poems)
~~A Better Life. 1989.~~
***Dialogue on Meditation-From the Quiet Place-A Kind of Believing**

1.6 Photographs

Illustration 1: Albert Meares with his sons Ainslie (the eldest; 10 yo) and Lindsay. Around 1920. Photographer unknown.

Illustration 2: Eva Meares, Ainslie Meares mother, around 1920. Photographer unknown. Image digitally repaired by S. Bruhn.

Illustration 3: Ainslie Meares at his home. Photographer Unknown. Image digitally repaired by S. Bruhn.

2. Relief Without Drugs By Ainslie Meares

How you can overcome tension, anxiety and pain.

A Prominent Australian Psychiatrist presents a way to defeat the stresses and strains of modern life

Believing that many modern doctors have encouraged people to turn too quickly to sedatives or tranquilisers, **Dr Ainslie Meares** presents a "do-it-yourself"method for the relief of nervous tension and anxieties and the control of pain. In his book, **Relief Without Drugs (RWD)**, he describes step-by-step simple techniques that can be practised by anyone, at any time. This self-management involves the complete relaxation of both body and mind. The causes and the signs of anxiety and many interesting facts about the nature of pain, are also set out in **Relief Without Drugs**

Background

This distilled version of **Relief Without Drugs** captures the essence of the original book. It is a snapshot of Meares method (the "Relaxing Mental Exercise") and writing in the 1960s. At the time, the hippy and feminist movements were new and unconventional. Meares wrote for the audience of the day using language they would understand. For that reason, **RWD** was politically correct (for its time) and some editorial adjustments have been made but readers should bear this in mind.

Originally, many short comments were inserted into the **RWD** text incorporating Meares' later work. All this did was interrupt the flow and reduced its cohesion. A few comments were retained. Most were placed after **RWD** in S3 entitled **After RWD** reflecting the refinements made by Meares over the following decades.

2.1 Introduction

Feelings of tension and anxiety seem all too common in today's hectic and complex world. Perhaps you cannot describe too well exactly what the feeling is. But I am sure you will recognise some of the symptoms I am going to describe.

Anxiety or tension may not be very severe – perhaps nothing more than a kind of restlessness, or a slight nervousness in social situations or at work. Perhaps you find yourself getting a little too impatient too often. You wife or husband, your children, your friends may complain that you are on edge.

Perhaps you have trouble concentrating, or have vague feelings of fear, without quite knowing what you are afraid of. Your nervous tension may show itself in a stiff, unnatural way of walking, or in the way you speak. Perhaps you have trouble falling asleep, or sleep comes in short, unsatisfying patches.

Everybody feels some of these symptoms in one degree or another at some time. You may have become so used to being in a tense or anxious state that you don't even recognise it as unnatural.

I am going to describe to you a way of dealing with anxiety that may seem almost too simple to believe. It is, in fact, the most natural way of improving the mental and bodily sense of well-being.

My method for relieving anxiety and tension requires only that you learn how to relax your body and your mind. And you can learn to do this. You can learn by practising a simple Relaxing Mental Exercise that I am going to describe later – this can be done at any time and in any place.

As you become increasingly able to do this successfully, you will have an increasing ability to let your body relax and you mind regress to a simpler less distressed state.

All are familiar, too, with pain. A session at the dentist may be painful. Childbirth is painful. A burn or a cut brings pain. Or you may suffer from some bodily disorder that puts you in constant and extreme discomfort. The Relaxing Mental Exercise can bring you to a state of ease in which, although, the pain is not removed, you experience no hurt or distress from it.

Pain: A Warning

I must give you a clear, unequivocal warning: **Pain fulfils a biologically important function.**

It serves as a signal that all is not well with the body, and calls for rest, or some remedial action. Without the signal of pain people would continue on their way, and damaged or inflamed tissues would be subject to further injury. **So it is important to be quite clear what is causing the pain before relieving it.**

But pain is often unnecessarily severe and then becomes an injuring influence itself. In these cases' relief of the pain not only saves the individual suffering but hastens the reparative process by conserving the patient's strength.

The biological significance of nervous tension is not so obvious. But whereas pain acts as a warning that all is not well with the body, anxiety warns that all is not well in the mind. When people have too much to do, too many decisions to make, they experience anxiety in the form of nervous tension, and are warned to do less. This situation arises more commonly when some moral decision is involved or when something links the present problem with some similar experience in the past which has not gone well.

Suffering is reduced by the relief of anxiety, because the person with anxiety really suffers from his mental turmoil, and the relief of anxiety in itself helps to restore normal mental functioning. If, however, after a reasonable trial of the Relaxing Mental Exercise described later, the signs of anxiety should persist, and particularly if they are associated with feelings of depression, then you should consult your doctor with a view to possible psychiatric treatment.

2.2 The Nature of Anxiety

What is anxiety? Here are some general statements that help define it.

The Physical Basis

The brain is continually receiving a great number of nervous impulses. Some are conscious, but the great majority are unconscious. These impulses arise from three different areas – from the person's external environment, from the body itself, and from the mind. All these impulses have to be dealt with and integrated to allow the smooth working of the brain. If the number of impulses becomes too great, the brain is unable to comply. There is in fact a level at which integration of the impulses becomes incomplete, and this is experienced as anxiety.

How The Body And Mind Respond

The body reacts to anxiety with a number of physiological responses. The heart rate is increased, blood pressure rises, blood is diverted from the organs to the muscles, and the pupils of the eyes are dilated. The body prepares to meet some emergency. It is really a preparation for action – for fight or flight. This biologically ancient reaction is inherited from times when dangers were usually a threat of physical attack.

But, in fact, the beating of the heart and tensing of muscles for physical action only tends to increase anxiety, because there is no outward foe whom we can vent the physical strength which has been mobilised.

The mind becomes very alert, too alert, so that all the time it seems to be searching for the cause of its own disquiet. There develops a pathological over alertness. Thus a noise which would normally go unheard causes an anxious person to start.

This over alertness shows itself in many ways. The individual is on the lookout all the time. He is fidgety and cannot let himself go off guard. He cannot rest because his mind keeps him alert even when there is no need for it. To relax and sit still becomes a near impossibility.

Sometimes, however, another type of reaction takes place so that the anxious individual is dulled and apathetic – as in an overwhelming national or personal disaster..

The person is "struck dumb", "in a daze", "unable to think or move". This comes about by the over activity of the self regulatory mechanisms of the body. There is a surge of anxiety with its accompanying over alertness, but if this were too great the body would be overwhelmed and unable to respond effectively. To prevent this, the self regulatory mechanisms come into play and inhibit the anxiety of the inhibiting mechanism that causes the individual to be tired, listless, dull, apathetic, and unable to take effective action.

The Individual Response

Most people when they experience anxiety take heed of the warning and do something about it. They do a little less work and so reduce the stream of impulses to the brain, or take a holiday away from disturbing conflicts, or rest and give the brain a chance to re-establish equilibrium or take sedatives and tranquillising drugs. This works well enough when the major inflow of disturbing impulses comes from outside sources, but it is generally ineffective when it arises in the unconscious mind. It is then that the Relaxing Mental Exercise described later is needed.

Common Signs Of Anxiety

Everybody experiences nervous tension of some degree at some time, and all are familiar with the more obvious signs of anxiety. However, there is a multitude of ways in which anxiety may manifest itself, and some mislead both patient and doctor to believe the trouble is due to some organic (bodily) cause rather than to the disordered function of the mind.

Anxiety In The Mind

Apprehension. This state of mind is anxiety in pure form. There is the feeling of fear, but the person knows there is nothing to make him afraid. If the anxiety is severe, this irrational element may evoke feelings of approaching insanity, and disquiet of the mind is increased. In less severe form, apprehension may show itself as a vague uneasiness.

Nervous tension. Nervous tension is a less complicated sensation than apprehension – though they may both occur

45

together – and lacks the feeling of impending disaster. The sufferer feels tense in the mind, the brain, or the whole self. Relaxation seems impossible. He feels wound-up like a spring and cannot let go.

This nervous tension of anxiety is often accompanied by physical muscle tension.

Minor degrees of nervous tension show themselves in the way people function in everyday life. There is a lack of ease. Even in walking, the arms do not swing in the accustomed fashion, and the gait has the appearance of being strained and awkward. Sometimes these symptoms of anxiety very closely resemble those of organic illness. There is a tendency to talk abruptly and too quickly. In writing, the pen is held too tightly. The hand starts to shake, the writing becomes jerky.

Irritability. Anxiety commonly shows itself in irritability. People react too quickly and too much to minor frustrations.

Insomnia. Poor sleep is the rule for the anxious individual. There is difficulty in falling asleep. It seems impossible to get comfortable, and he tosses and turns and worries.

Sleep is commonly disturbed by frightening dreams, so he wakes in a sweat with a pounding heart and the other physiological signs of anxiety.

Fatigue. As one would expect from the over-alertness, nervous tension, and lack of sleep, fatigue is a constant symptom of anxiety. However, where the normal fatigue of a day of mental and physical activity leads to contented rest, the fatigue of anxiety is restless, alert, and lacks the pleasant relaxing quality of normal tiredness.

Depression. It is important to consider the matter of depression carefully. Depression may be caused through anxiety, loss, or bereavement, in which case it can be relieved by the technique I am about to describe; on the other hand, it may result from a quite different type of nervous illness which is best treated by other means. If the sense of depression is sufficiently severe to bring the feeling that life is not worth living, or if fleeting thoughts of suicide come to mind, or if the depression is accompanied by feelings that you are somehow being punished for your past sins, then it is important that you consult your doctor.

Lack of concentration. Students and those whose occupation requires steady brain-work often find that their anxiety shows itself primarily in lack of concentration (common at exam time). Others may notice inability to concentrate when reading, or even in conversation with friends.

Difficulties with friends. Anxiety often shows itself in difficulty in interpersonal relations. The anxious one is no longer at ease when meeting people, even those he knows. Oddly enough, professional and business dealings with people are more easily handled than social occasions, even when the social occasion is of no consequence. The reason is that in professional and business dealings there is something definite to do. But small talk (ie social chit chat) is more difficult.

This difficulty in interpersonal relationships resulting from anxiety may come between husband and wife or young lovers, cutting off the free interchange of their emotion. In a similar way the anxious mother may become separated from her baby; the infant, in animal fashion, senses her tension and reacts to it.

Restlessness. The anxious patient cannot sit still. He cannot settle to the task in hand; he starts one job, leaves it, and starts something else. He is restless when there is something definite that he has to do, so he is more comfortable at work than at home. On weekends, in spite of happy relations with his family, it is common for him to wish for Monday and the routine of work.

Some people with anxiety are benefited by a holiday, but when restlessness is a feature the anxious patient only returns more tense and frustrated than ever.

Phobias. In a phobia, the patient remains reasonably at ease until confronted with the phobic situation. He then experiences discomfort which may vary from mild apprehension to uncontrollable panic. The patient develops a fear of the particular situation which causes him this distress, and the condition is known as a phobia. Common phobias are heights, being away from home, being in crowds, or being in enclosed spaces such as lifts. Knives, swords, and firearms often become the objects of phobias. In a similar way people may develop an irrational fear of certain animals such as mice, cats, moths. The sufferer is always aware that his phobia is irrational, but this does nothing at all to relieve his sense of panic.

Obsessional tension. People evolve their own ways of coping with tension. Some relieve it by "blowing their top" and ventilating their emotion, and in this way they dissipate their anxiety; some develop a studied calm; while with others the anxiety is concentrated in one particular limb or organ, so that the rest of the body is free. Other people cope with inner tension by making sure that they have everything just right. The feel is that if everything is right there can be nothing to worry about. This is likely to become an obsession with them so that they become pre-occupied with it and spend much of their time checking things over time and again. The need to have things just right leads to doubts about whether things are right or not. In this way the obsessive is continually in doubt, so that he becomes a constant worrier, and even trivial decisions may become a matter of great effort. If something upsets his set routines, he becomes tense and anxious.

Stuttering. Anxiety may have an effect on stuttering. In the right-handed person the left side of the brain is dominant over the right, and as a result the right hand is given preference over the left. In those who are left-handed the right side of the brain is dominant over the left. It is believed that stuttering often develops when the dominance of the leading side of the brain is incomplete, or when a potentially left handed child is trained to function as a right hander. Stuttering results when the messages from the brain to the organ of speech are indecisive. This indecision may be increased by anxiety.

But some people stutter without showing or feeling much tension or anxiety at all. As a general rule, these do not gain much help in their speech difficulty by practising Relaxing Mental Exercise. However, the majority of stutterers do.

Anxiety In The Body

Palpitation. One of the commonest symptoms of anxiety is the abnormal awareness of the action of the heart which is due to hypersensitivity rather than over-activity of the organ itself. The individual comes to feel there is something wrong with the heart, and reassurance is difficult while his anxiety remains.

Pain near the heart. Anxiety frequently produces pain in the left side of the chest which patients immediately suspect to be due to some disease of the heart. However, the pain of anxiety is usually situated well to the left of where the pain from organic disease would be, and there are other differences.

Nervous dyspepsia. Discomfort in the stomach felt beneath the ribs in the upper part of the abdomen is one of the commonest signs of anxiety. The discomfort – or, if it is more severe, the pain – is very similar in nature to the pain of peptic ulcer, except that the pain of nervous dyspepsia tends to be associated with emotional stress, whereas ulcer pain is more clearly related to food intake.

Constipation. The normal response of the body to anxiety includes a dampening down of movement of the bowels. A mild anxiety reaction over a long period may lead to chronic constipation.

Nervous diarrhoea. The self-regulating mechanisms of the body may come into action in an attempt to restore equilibrium. It is quite common for the self-regulating mechanisms to overcompensate. When this happens there is increased mobility of the bowel, and diarrhoea results instead of constipation.

In sexual life. The tense or anxious woman commonly has a loss of both desire and response.

Young men are quite prone to sexual anxiety. This is an entirely psychological reaction, and virile appearance or athletic build are no armour against it. The anxiety often arises in an early experience which has been unsuccessful because of guilt. On subsequent occasions the anxiety is rekindled and the pattern of failure becomes even more firmly established. Older men also may be affected in a similar way by anxieties arising from non-sexual conflicts.

Asthma. Allergy, infection, genetic constitution and emotional influences are important factors in bronchial asthma.

However, preoccupation with allergy in the past 20 or 30 years has led to the neglect of the emotional factors, which are much more elusive and harder to appreciate as an aspect of science. But the importance of the emotional influence is beyond all doubt.

I have had a number of patients who suffered for years from classical asthma, with proven sensitivity to common pollens and dusts. They ceased to have attacks of asthma after being treated by relaxing methods (that is, when their anxiety was reduced), even though they were still exposed to the same pollens and dusts which in the past had caused the attacks.

Nervous rashes. Emotional stresses in the mind are apt to produce nervous rashes in the skin. Self-management of these nervous rashes involves reduction both in the level of anxiety and responsiveness to emotional stress.

Headaches and migraine. These two different conditions are both associated with anxiety – nervous headache directly so, and migraine less directly.

Painful monthly periods. There are physical conditions which pre-dispose towards this complaint, but nearly always there is an important emotional factor. If this can be remedied by reducing the patient's general level of anxiety so that she ceases to overreact to stress, the condition is usually cured of or greatly relieved.

In **Life Without Stress**[100] Meares made additional points about anxiety in the body including those below.

Muscle tension and the shakes. Overalertedness of the brain holds some muscle cells in contraction and eventually they fatigue and become sore. In the shakes, the overalertedness of the brain cells tricks the muscles and the shaking is the result.

Irritable bowel syndrome arises when the overactive brain cells respond to even mild stimulant qualities in food and the bowel over reacts with the irritable results.

Nervous urination has a similar mechanism to nervous diarrhoea

Spots before the eyes are also called muscae volitantes or floaters. They are actually tiny particles of harmless sediment inside the fluid filled eyeball. Movement of the head and the eye can agitate these floaters up into our line of sight. When anxiety results in overactive brain cells our visual perception is enhanced to such an extent that we see a spot (or sometimes spots).

Peptic ulcer. Nearly 20 years later, Meares wrote that anxiety could contribute to peptic ulcer and that Stillness Meditation could help the healing of peptic ulcer.

High blood pressure is essentially caused by the contraction of the smooth muscle cells in the walls of the arteries. This contraction reduces the size of the lumen or hole inside the artery which increases blood pressure. There are various factors that can contribute to high blood pressure (eg kidney or vascular disease etc), However, in the early stages it is worth trying Stillness Meditation to see whether the reduced sympathetic nervous system tone might significantly reduce or normalise the blood pressure.

Diaphragmatic hernia is a common xray finding in the

---

100 Life Without Stress, p58-60,69, 70, 72, 118

general population but trouble from it seems to depend upon the individuals nervous condition. Person commonly say that the trouble comes and goes. Due to the individuals nervous condition varying and affecting the perception of discomfort.

Ulcerative colitis an infectious condition of the large bowel with patches of ulceration of the lining. Anxiety may increase bowel movement. The squeezing action can then further damage the ulcerated areas. Meares observed that ulcerative colitis may dramatically improve with Stillness Meditation practice.

Problems of ill health unrelated to anxiety[101]. These are health problems that are <u>not</u> caused by anxiety and have some other cause. Meares noted these problems could result in a flow of nerve impulses from the affected part of the body to the brain. This added to the sum total of messages the brain had to integrate. It is the inability to integrate the nerve messages that results in anxiety. So, it can be seen that disease processes unrelated to anxiety can add a background of disturbing nerve impulses. This can also be added to if a person is worried about their health condition.

It works the other way as well. If the unrelated health condition flares up then the person may experience higher levels of anxiety. Meares example conditions included arthritis, prostatitis, viral infections (eg the flu), some skin conditions and fatigue secondary to some other disease process.

---

101 Life without Stress, pp27-31

2.3 Common Causes of Anxiety

Sexual Causes Of Tension

Nowadays there is a tendency to lay great emphasis on sex, and the tensions of both old and young are often ascribed (especially by amateur psychologists) to some disharmony in their sex life without due consideration of other facts. Now, sexual conflicts are a very important cause of anxiety, but conflicts in other areas are also important, and, in fact, anxiety often results from a sum total of stresses arising from various problems.

What makes it difficult to assess the significance of sexual troubles as a cause of anxiety is the fact that people like to give socially acceptable explanations – the businessman, for instance, will tell his doctor of his hard work and late hours when explaining his anxieties, but he does not readily discuss the tension arising from his emotional involvement with his secretary. He is ashamed to admit the real cause to the doctor.

In other cases, the patient may be too ashamed to admit the real cause even to himself. This applies to both sexes. It is common for boys and young men before marriage to suffer feelings of shame and guilt, and some remain disturbed even after their behaviour is explained. Nervous tension may be extremely severe.

Also, with reference to adolescence, the current fashion for frequent reference to homosexuality in literature, the theatre, films, etc, brings the idea of this aspect of life to the minds of many sensitive young people who would otherwise never have thought of it. They come to worry about it.

Sex and the shy adolescent. The shy introvert typically has greater difficulties in making the transition from childhood to maturity than his more robust extrovert contemporaries. Inclined to be timid and embarrassed by matters of sex, he withdraws from it, his uncertainties and perplexities increase, and the general level of his anxiety remains high. Yet experience shows the inhibited introvert of either sex is helped by talking the matter over with an experienced physician or psychiatrist.

Sex and marriage. Only a very mature person can go against the established behaviour pattern of his group without experiencing inner tension. A young person of either sex may become tense simply from the knowledge that his fellows are promiscuous. But what offends one may not offend another and, from the viewpoint of causing anxiety, there is no hard-and-fast rule. The censure of the group, either for being too free or not free enough, according to the prevailing morality of the group, causes tension. But the inner censor is difficult to quiet, and the idea of sexual experience for the sake of one's partner (though it may seem plausible at the time) does little to dispel subsequent tension and anxiety if it conflicts with the basic personality of the individual.

Some degree of anxiety from this type of situation, which arises, is almost universal among young people. (I speak as a doctor, concerned with anxiety and tension – there may be others who would speak from a different viewpoint.)

Contraception and anxiety. The ready availability of reliable oral contraception has undoubtedly been a significant factor in relieving tens of thousands of women from tension and anxiety. On the other hand, the advent of the contraceptive pill has brought tension and guilt to many women who might otherwise have been free of it.

If a woman believes contraception is morally wrong, or if she is forbidden by her church to use it and follows her conscience and does not use it, she may still suffer considerable tension from knowing that women all round her are using contraception.

The position is much more difficult when husband and wife disagree on the matter. She may have contraception forced on her without consideration of her religious feelings.

Another important social side effect of the pill is that promiscuous girls are now relieved of much of their anxiety. Also, the pill has undoubtedly led many girls into promiscuity, and many of these suffer nervous tension caused by moral qualms about their new way of life.

Fear of pregnancy. This is one of the most common causes of anxiety in women of child-bearing age. The unmarried woman who has let herself be led into a foolish sexual experience without proper contraceptive precautions inevitably experiences severe tension. The married woman who fears pregnancy usually says it would be financially embarrassing or would interfere with her social life, but it frequently turns out to be based on a deep-seated fear of childbirth, which perhaps developed from foolish talk by her mother or elder sister. These women are not reassured by contraceptive measures and their intimate life with their husband leaves them cold and in constant tension.

Other sexual causes of tension arise when the sexual appetite of the partners is ill-matched, or when one partner is emotionally remote.

Aggression And Anxiety

Man's aggression has led him to master the other animal species and has to a large extent enabled him to control his immediate environment. However, civilisation has removed the opportunity to vent open aggression on animals that threaten him or on a neighbouring tribe who would take his food or his woman. Man's struggle with his own aggression is one of the greatest causes of tension, though he may not be aware of this.

Manifestations of aggression. A man is angered; he goes to strike another, but is withheld by his friends. In such a simple situation you can see how his aggression was mobilised and how it found direct expression. But, aggression is constantly manifesting itself in much more devious ways: the indifferent manner of the civil servant toward the public; one's own authoritative attitude to the shop assistant. When people talk too loudly or too quickly on a subject that affects them, it is aggression which motivates them. In fact, aggression is continually influencing behaviour in an emotional way in all the small facets of everyday life. If a person looks for it, he soon recognises it in friends, and with a little introspection is humiliated to find the same force within himself.

Aggression in childhood and adolescence. The beginnings of this aggression element can be seen in early infancy. Baby is happy when mother's milk comes freely and easily, but if it does not he is frustrated, and in a moment we see anger in his face, and his aggression is vented in crying and generalised movements of his body.

One child's aggression may be aroused by a degree of parental discipline that would be easily tolerated by another. Anything which serves to make the child different from his fellows may arouse his aggression. When basic cultural or religious factors work to separate the family from others in the district, the child often suffers a smouldering aggressive reaction and his childhood may be marred by chronic anxiety and tension.

The adolescent is angered if he is still treated as a boy. This arouses aggression. To prove he is grown-up he becomes defiant and unconsciously sets about to show the world that no one can tell him what he must do. The company of other young men with impulsive aggression like his own provides an easy milieu for the dissipation of his aggression; thus the genesis of the teenage gang.

Control of aggression. It may simply be dissipated, as when a child is thwarted by his parents. His aggression is aroused, but he cannot give it direct expression or he will be punished. His aggression is dissipated as he stamps about, handles his toys roughly, etc. In a more sophisticated way adults dissipate aggression by playing games or by watching sports in which they identify themselves with the players and experience their emotions.

Aggression can also be displaced, so that aggressive impulses toward one person or situation are vented on some completely innocent party. The husband is frustrated at work by his boss. His aggression is aroused. He cannot give it direct expression, but on reaching home he blows up and vents it on his unsuspecting wife.

Aggression can also be controlled by act of will. But this control, and the awareness of the necessity for it, creates a further stress, and the individual is tense and anxious as a result.

The person who is controlling a good deal of aggression is vulnerable to minor additional stresses. This is an important factor in the cause of bad temper. Father tolerates the bickering of the children for a long time, then he suddenly blows up and punishes them more severely than he intended.

Aggression need not be a destructive force. The same impulse that drives a man to feel like punching someone in the nose can be diverted and used to drive him on in life to achieve goals in commerce, industry, science, or artistic fields.

Anxiety is the price paid when victory over aggression is incomplete. So, the individual must aim to establish a pattern of life in which overt aggression is not easily aroused. He can do this by understanding the factors involved, using native aggression in creative fashion, and by practising Relaxing Mental Exercise which give ease of mind.

Anxiety And Insecurity

People are basically insecure, and this is the root of much anxiety. They can never hope for real material security. At any moment, even in the most protected situations, they may be stricken down with illness or death. As man has learned to doubt, the security of religious belief has ebbed from him, and as a result his latent anxiety and tension is so much the worse.

Childhood insecurity. Children are insecure because of their relative weakness compared with those about them. This childhood feeling of insecurity may persist and form a pattern of tension and anxious behaviour in adult life.

An interesting point is that the child withstands the evil influence of a constantly hostile environment better than he does an inconsistent one, where those around him are changeable, sometimes harsh and sometimes loving. In the latter circumstances the child does not know what to expect, and as a result lives in a state of chronic anxiety.

At school the child may be subject to subtle influences which further increase his insecurity. The native aggressive impulses of children are easily turned on some less fortunate member of the group. Minor degrees of bullying may take a form that is scarcely perceptible to adults, but at the same time may produce chronic tension in the unfortunate victim.

Insecurity at work. Man has evolved to what he is today through hundreds of thousands of years of insecurity. In fact, it would seem he functions best when not completely secure.

At work there is always insecurity. A man may lose his job, or his business may fail. If this insecurity reaches a certain degree he becomes tense and anxious. The sensitive are among the first affected, and those who are less gifted, less competent, and less well trained soon feel the strain. The situation is always worse when aggression is aroused. Because of insecurity, aggression has to be controlled at work, and as a result is likely to be displaced on to a wife and children at home.

Insecurity at home. Home is not always a refuge, a haven from the storms of the outside world. Tension in the home is a familiar theme. Sexual difficulties and the displacement of the husband's aggression on to his wife are common enough. But often simple insecurity is an important factor in the wife's nervous tension.

She is insecure because she does not know how her husband will react. He is a different man according to whether he has had a good day or a bad day at the office, or whether he has had a few drinks on the way home.

There is obvious insecurity when the marriage is about to break up. But there are many less clearly defined actions which produce the same unease. The subtle change of attitude, the defensive reply, the inconsequential greeting, the vague reasons for this or that, and above all a lessening of sexual demands even when she herself has no particular sexual desire; these may all combine to produce a state of sub clinical insecurity in the wife. She becomes chronically tense and ill at ease, perhaps not knowing exactly why.

Anxiety From Personality Traits

The perfectionist and anxiety. The perfectionist unconsciously tries to ward off his inner tension by having everything just right. His efforts to be perfectly neat, scrupulously conscientious, and meticulously clean soon bring worries of their own, and the perfectionist comes to live a rigid and rather constricted way of life with a constantly high level of mental tension.

These difficulties are so much the more accentuated if the perfectionist is married to, or works with, a person who is freer and less restricted. Then he is constantly ill at ease, wanting to clean up after his disorderly companion so that he can once again have everything just right.

Anxiety and dependence. Children are dependent upon parents for physical survival, so a pattern of accepting dependence is ingrained at an early stage.

Although they grow up into relatively independent adults, a need for some degree of dependence persists. This is more obvious in the character of a woman, and has the biological function of allowing her to accept dependence when it is necessary for her during her childbearing period. On the other hand, the idea of being dependent on others may conflict with the aggressive and self-assertive aspects of a man's personality. Such men want to be independent of their parents of their wife, but at the same time they feel the need for dependency. As a result they feel a tension for which they can see no reason.

Another cause of tension concerns the need to be depended

upon. It is not uncommon for an emotionally mature woman to marry a man less mature than herself. He comes to rely on her and to be dependent upon her. She in turn enjoys giving this support from the fullness of her maturity. However, it often happens when the couple have their first baby that the wife switches and puts the child's need for dependence on her first. The husband becomes tense! He is not quite sure what has happened.

On the other hand, a man who is a little immature may have fought hard to become independent of his parents in spite of his deep-seated wish to remain dependent. He succeeds, and has the feeling of well-being because his independence satisfies his masculinity. However, if such a man marries a mature, motherly type of woman, as he is often unconsciously driven to do, he may become tense again, because she, without knowing it, tries to develop a dependent relationship with him, which he unconsciously wants but at the same time strives to avoid.

Anxiety and Intelligence. People of less intelligence, and with less well-integrated minds, find many ordinary everyday tasks quite difficult, while other more gifted people do these things naturally and easily without giving the matter any particular thought. The less gifted are therefore under a constant stress which others are not. As a result they remain tense, but are usually unable to see the cause.

Of course, this situation is relative. A highly intelligent person who is doing a job requiring exceptionally high intelligence experiences the same tensions as a dull person does in a less exacting job. Similarly, the intellectually backward individual may learn to live a useful and happy life as long as he can work and live in an environment which is not too demanding for him.

A disparity of intelligence between husband and wife may be a constant source of tension, especially when the wife is the more gifted one. Unless she is a very perceptive woman, this disparity will lead her into a dominant role in the household which is likely to clash with her husband's masculinity and so produce further tension.

Anxiety and conscience. Very simple problems of conscience can produce tension in quite a surprising fashion. It is common clinical experience to find that patients are tense on account of some problem of tax evasion. It is usually not so much a matter of frank dishonesty but rather a problem of stretching the loopholes of the law to such an extent that inner conscience becomes uneasy.

Sensitive introvert people may become overwhelmed by the material values that they find around them only to become aware that they themselves are lacking in any spiritual goal.

Every sensitive individual, man or woman, if he is to remain free from inner tension, must make for himself some way of life which satisfies these vague needs of conscience and idealism.

2.4 Self Management of Anxiety

General Principles

Many causes of anxiety can, in fact, be remedied. This, of course, is the first step in the self-management of anxiety. Those causes that have a basis in external reality are the easiest to remedy.

But many causes of anxiety are simply there and cannot be escaped. Understanding the origin of these, combined with a calm and easy acceptance of the situation helps.

Tensions due to unknown causes are much more difficult to tolerate. Actually, in the vast majority of cases, little can be done to modify the causes of tension, and the book is primarily directed to this type of case. The approach is through Relaxing Mental Exercise.

Do not be put off by the simplicity of what I recommend. It is **natural** as well as **simple**, and that is why it is so successful.

Relaxation. There is a close relationship between bodily tension and the sensation of mental tension. Worry makes the body tense, but relax the body very completely and the mind soon begins to feel relaxed.

A basic principle of the Relaxing Mental Exercise is the use of **physical relaxation as a key to mental relaxation**. This takes place in two stages. First, the individual must learn complete physical relaxation, and, second, learn how to use this physical relaxation to promote calm and ease of mind. The mind relaxes following the relaxation of the body, and this mental relaxation tends to persist after the body has ceased to relax. As the process is repeated, the mental relaxation becomes more prolonged, until finally it stays with the patient in his everyday tasks.

Relaxing Mental Exercise **is effective irrespective of the cause of anxiety.**

At present there is a popular belief that the only really satisfactory way to treat nervous illness is to unearth the cause. A little thought shows that this is simply not true. Many people recover from nervous illness when they are given appropriate drugs, and religious experience, meditation, and philosophical practices have brought peace of mind to many who were disturbed.

Furthermore, every psychiatrist knows that many patients can be brought to a full knowledge of conflicts which caused their condition, but their symptoms still remain.

Conditioning. Relaxing Mental Exercise works by conditioning the individual to a state of calm and ease of mind. It becomes the means of learning a new pattern of response to certain situations – the response of calm and ease of mind.

The idea of regression. Before learning a new pattern of response, the patient must first regress – go back in his mind to the state before the development of the bad pattern of response. In the Relaxing Mental Exercise this is done. The patient regresses to a state of mind free from anxiety and is then free to learn the new pattern of calm and ease of mind.

This is basically why explanation and persuasion are generally ineffective. The patient can see the logic, but he probably remains as tense and anxious as ever. But if the mind regresses to a state free from anxiety it is free to learn a new pattern of ease and calm. Also, integration of the impulses arriving at the brain is aided.

Some Practical Considerations

There are a number of practical points which I always explain very carefully to patients.

Do not expect too much too quickly.

Be prepared for ups and downs.

Do not be impatient with yourself when at first you cannot relax. Relaxation is not difficult, but if you could do it in two minutes there would be no need for my detailed instructions.

Bring yourself to like mental exercise. The attitude of the mind is quite important.

Mental exercise is similar to physical exercise. Everyone accepts the idea of doing physical exercise to promote physical health. The present procedure is merely a matter of doing mental exercise to promote mental health.

Keep the feeling of relaxation during your everyday tasks.

Posture

The actual posture of the body has quite an influence on the effect of the mental exercise. And **it is better to practice when fresh and alert.**

Posture should not be too comfortable. Most people believe that the more comfortable one is, the more effective will be his relaxation. This idea is quite wrong. If one lies down comfortably on one's bed, relaxation comes relatively easily. But this type of relaxation has little effect in relieving tension. What is aimed for here is mental relaxation which comes from the mind itself. In order to achieve this one must not be too comfortable.

Use a symmetrical posture. Whether patients lie down, or sit, or squat, mental relaxation is more effective in a symmetrical posture, with arms and legs in similar positions on each side of the body.

Lying. This is the basic posture and the easiest for the exercise. Simply lie on the back with arms by the sides. Young people do not need a pillow. Adults can use a low pillow, but the lower the better, as lying quite flat enhances the feeling of abandonment – the letting go – which is such an important part of mental relaxation.

At the start a couch is quite suitable; but as soon as real feeling of relaxation is attained it is wise to transfer to the harder floor.

Sitting. This is generally best for asthmatics and for middle-aged subjects. At first, it is wise to use an armchair so that the arms can rest comfortably on the sides of the chair. It is best to sit up in the chair rather straight, without the body slumped, which could tend to make the position too comfortable. The head can rest on the back of the chair. The legs are bent at the knees, and women find it wise to remove high-heeled shoes.

When a fair degree of relaxation can be attained in an armchair, try a straight-backed dining-room chair. The head is now unsupported, and the fore-arms rest comfortably on the thighs.

Squatting. Sit on a cushion **cross-legged** on the floor. Arms can hang loosely at the sides or rest in the groins. The whole of the head, neck, and back is unsupported.

Try to keep the back and the neck fairly straight so that the muscular effort to maintain the position is reduced to a minimum. The cross-legged position usually makes enough tension on the joints to induce mild discomfort. As a result of these factors, relaxation attained in this posture is usually very effective. The position is very satisfactory for youthful subjects and those who suffer from asthma, as it makes for easier breathing than lying down.

When And Where To Do The Exercise

Fit them into your way of life in as natural a way as possible. At first, do them in circumstances in which you yourself feel secure. Otherwise you cannot let yourself go off guard. This is important in the initial stages; then, as you become more secure, you can do them almost anywhere. Most men do them for five minutes before leaving for work, and then for a longer period after the evening meal. The housewife finds it best to do them after she has got her husband off to work and the children to school. There is no need to be alone while doing them.

About 10 minutes twice a day is all the time required.

A good way is to **let the mental exercise become a routine habit.** I have had several patients who have made them part of the routine of the morning shower. Come out of the shower; get dry; with the towel around you sit on a stool, on the side of the bath, or squat on the floor – just for 3 minutes – and feel the relaxation all through you.

Some people like doing the exercise while sitting outside in the open air. The sun is on the face, wind blows the hair, distant sounds are heard; they let go, and all this aids the calm and integration within.

How Long To Keep Doing The Exercise

People have sometimes asked how long they should keep doing the exercise. I suppose the answer is "As long as it is doing you good". But don't just drop it at the first sign that your symptoms are subsiding.

Later on Meares recommended ongoing daily practice.

How To Do The Exercise

Sit in an armchair or lie down on a couch flat on your back. Eyes are comfortably closed. Think to yourself.

It is good to relax.
Relaxing is natural.
It is the natural way to calm and ease.

Relaxing The Body

Bring the body into relaxation by allowing the tension to go from the muscles, allowing your muscles to let go. As you do this, keep aware of the relaxation. In fact, this conscious awareness of the relaxed and easy feeling is a very important part of the exercise.

It is best to start with the big muscles of the thighs and arms because it is easiest to feel the relaxation in them.

Test this now, as you are sitting reading this book. Just let your hand rest on the thigh. Now go to straighten your leg, but do not move it. With your hand you will feel the muscles of your thigh contract. Then you allow the muscles to let go, and with your hand you feel them relax. Now do the same thing without your hand on your thigh. You are still aware of the muscles first contracting and then letting go. Sometimes, just at first, it is hard to capture this feeling of letting go. But if you do this two or three times you will soon come to feel it.

Now start on the exercise. Present these ideas to your mind:

We think of our legs,
the muscles of our legs.
We allow them to let go.
We can feel them relax, we really feel it.
The muscles of our legs let go.
They let go so that all we feel of our legs
is the weight of them on the floor.
They are heavy and comfortable
the natural weight of our legs.
We feel this easy comfortable relaxation come all through us.
Feel it in our body.
Our arms are heavy on the side of the chair.
They are so relaxed we just feel the weight of them.
The natural weight of them.
Natural.
It is all natural.
Natural to let ourselves relax,
and our mind learns to be calm and at ease again.
We feel the relaxation more and more.
It grows on us.
Our arms are so relaxed they hardly seem to belong to us.
Our whole body is relaxed.
We feel ourselves sitting in the chair.
Sinking into the chair.

We feel it in the face.
The muscles of our face relax with it.
Our jaw is loose.
It is so relaxed, so loose that our lips part.
We feel it in the muscles around our eyes.
We feel the muscles of our face smooth out with the relaxation.
It is in our forehead.
At the sides of our forehead,
we feel it there deeply.

These are ideas to present to the mind. Do not just say them over, or repeat the thoughts. It is much more than that. These ideas all concern feeling. **Have the idea in your mind, and at the time bring yourself to experience the appropriate feeling.**

You are in fact experiencing both the feeling and the act. Thus, the muscles of the legs let go, and you feel them let go. But the relationship of the act and the feeling is more complicated than this. You feel relaxed, and you are relaxed. It is natural and easy. Feeling and doing in this context are essentially simple and primitive. You have the idea of your muscles relaxing. Then you experience it – really experience it – without the intervention of critical thought.

Repeat this exercise a number of times, and the feeling of relaxation becomes more and more a reality. But in repeating it – remember – there is no hurry, no rush; the whole thing is leisurely, easy, natural.

The sequence of the parts of the exercise follow quite naturally, so that they are easy enough to remember: the relaxation of the legs, the body, the arms, the face, and its different parts.

Remember that it does not all come at once. If at first you can capture just some of the feelings, the others will soon follow. Try to experience the sensation of weight in the legs as the muscles relax and let go, so that the legs seem heavy on the floor. The feeling of the face smoothing out as the facial muscles relax is another part of the exercise which comes quite easily. This is felt in the relaxation of the muscles around the eyes, and is enhanced by the letting go of the muscles of the jaw and the parting of the lips.

Relaxing The Mind

As already explained, relaxation of the body itself produces some relaxation of the mind. But one can go further than that, and continue the exercise in this fashion:

Our whole body is relaxed.
We feel it all through us.
It is in our face.
Our face is utterly relaxed.
Feel it in our forehead,
and in the sides of our forehead.
We feel it there deeply,
deeply in the sides of our forehead.
Deeply, we feel it in our mind.

This sequence follows on easily enough. One feels the relaxation in the muscles of the face, and feels the face smooth out in calm. There is a very intimate relationship between the state of the mind and the state of the face. If our mind is calm, so is our face. Conversely, if you learn to make your face calm, you experience a feeling of increasing calm of mind.

With the jaw loose, the muscles that work the jaw are fully relaxed. The two temporal muscles extend up to the sides of the forehead. You can feel them by placing the fingertips at the side of the forehead and firmly clenching the jaw. You can feel the muscles contract and then let go as the jaw is relaxed. The feeling of relaxation here gives the feeling of relaxation within – in the mind itself.

The whole of our body is relaxed.
We feel the relaxation of all the muscles
of our body.
They are relaxed.
They are relaxed and calm.
We can feel the calm.
We feel the relaxation and we feel the calm.
The relaxation is all through us,
and so is the calm that goes with it.
The calm of it is part of us.
It is all through us in our body and in our mind.

Remember that the feeling of relaxation may at first come and go. This is to be expected for the first few attempts. Remember that people who can attain relaxation of the body can all learn to attain relaxation of the mind. If you are able to capture just a moment of calm, it will not be long before you can achieve the full state.

Remember too, that relaxation of the mind is greatly enhanced by physical relaxation which is attained in relatively uncomfortable circumstances. So as you become more adept at physical relaxation you do it in increasingly uncomfortable positions.

Achieving Regression

When you have attained relaxation of your mind, you have already started on the way to regression.

This regression is quite a normal process. All experience it in moments of quiet reverie, ceasing to be alert and critical, with mind working at a simpler and more primitive level of organisation.

Continue the exercise, allowing yourself to neglect what is going on around you. Temporarily abandon the critical faculties. If a truck passes in the street, don't think of it as being a heavily laden truck going past in the street; it is just a noise. This is what I mean by allowing yourself to be uncritical.

Now proceed:

We feel the calm of it all through us.
We feel it in our body;
We feel it in our mind.
The calm pervades us.
We let ourselves go.
We let go, and we drift.
We drift in the calm of it.
Just letting ourselves go,
We drift more and more.

We let ourselves go with it.
We let ourselves go
more and more completely.
We let go ourselves,
more and still more completely.

You feel yourself drifting in the calm that is all about you. The drifting sensation does not usually come all at once. At first, there are moments of drifting. Then it stops, and you let go again, and the drifting returns. When this drifting sensation is achieved, one has regressed.

This is the general outline of the procedure. Each individual will make modifications to suit the particular needs of his own personality, his particular symptoms, and the particular circumstances in which he is situated. **It is important to get into the routine of just presenting the various ideas to the mind**. Do not think about the ideas in logical fashion, as this prevents regression.

Difficulties In Physical Relaxation

These are not great. The most common one is undoubtedly the simple reluctance of many people to try it. I have had so many people say to me, "I really did not think that this would be any good for me, but you talked me into trying it, and now I am already feeling much easier in myself."

Another difficulty is that some people find it hard to believe that anything so simple and so natural could help them when they have already tried dozens of tables and injections without effect.

Restlessness may be a difficulty. You sit down ready to start, and immediately want to move about. You fidget. You want move a leg and then an arm. Then you are aware that your clothes are uncomfortable, and move again. This is only an initial difficulty. If you have this trouble, make yourself as comfortable as you can. Use cushions; lie on a soft bed – anything that appeals to you as making you comfortable. Then do your relaxations; but do it only for a very short period- two or three minutes. After that have a rest and a stretch, and then do it again. Soon the phase of restlessness will pass, and then you can move into doing the exercise in more uncomfortable positions.

The feeling of physical discomfort in some part of the body- say, a leg- may cause difficulty on relaxation. At this stage, instead of moving the leg concentrate on relaxing more completely, in spite of the discomfort. The discomfort passes, and you relax more easily.

Sometimes a trembling of the muscles makes relaxation difficult. This is only a worry at the very start, and it soon passes. It is most common in the eyelids and the muscles around the eyes. In fact, some trembling of the eyelids would seem to be the general rule in the initial phases, and is of no consequence at all.

Difficulties Relaxing The Mind

It is extraordinary how people tend to give up even before they have started. "Relaxing the body, yes, I can do that; but relaxing my mind, that is impossible; that is why I have come to you." I hear this almost daily. Yet experience has shown that anyone who can achieve physical relaxation can likewise attain the sensation of relaxation of his mind, if he will only try – and try in the right way.

A common difficulty is that thoughts seem to become too active. One keeps thinking of the problems of the day. All the small inconsequential things of one's business keep running through the mind. You consciously turn your thoughts to your home. But the same thing happens again, and you become exasperated by the flow of unwanted thoughts. Cope with this difficulty simply by giving your thoughts full rein, letting them wander where they will without worrying about them. Just let the thoughts go, and there is no tension.

There is another approach to this same problem: Thinking of different parts of the body in turn, and making sure that each is relaxed.

I can feel my legs relaxed,
both of them relaxed.
My body, it is relaxed,
and I just feel the weight of it.
My arms relaxed,
my face smooth,
my jaw loose,
the muscles around my eyes relaxed,
my forehead relaxed deeply.

The sequence is then repeated easily and leisurely, starting with the legs again. Thus the mind is kept occupied so that other thoughts do not get the chance to intrude and worry you.

Difficulties In Regression

People are really rather afraid to let go – especially those who are tense and anxious.

Two things help. The first is to know that you are completely safe. This simple idea is of the utmost importance. It is perfectly safe for you to let yourself relax and go off guard, so that you mind can wander where it will.

The second way is to become more and more familiar with the sensation of letting go:

I feel the muscles of my legs let go.
The thighs and the calves, they really let go.
My arms let go so that they are just flopped on the sides of the chair.
And the muscles of my face, they let go.
My jaw has let go, I feel it loose.
And my face lets go so that I can feel it smooth out.
I let go my whole body.
I let myself go.
I just drift with it.

Some people experience difficulty in that they remain too alert to everything that is going on around them. The aim is to be oblivious of immediate surroundings. Help yourself like this:

I am just sitting here relaxing.
While I am doing it nothing else matters,
nothing else matters.
I am just here,
easy, comfortable, relaxed.
There is just me relaxing
Me relaxing, that is all that there is.

Some people as they start to relax, go straight to sleep. This is to be avoided. Sleep is some help in relieving tension but it is very, very much less help than this relaxed state of mind. **If you have a tendency to fall asleep when you start your exercise, use a more uncomfortable posture.** Do not lay down on a bed or sofa to practice.

More Advanced Exercise

Relaxing the eyelids. The eyelids are of particular importance. The anxious patient characteristically has his eyes wide open, so that the edge of the upper lid does not cover the top of the iris as it normally does. I have seen some patients with severe anxiety who have been so over alert that they have virtually found it impossible to allow their eyes to close even for a moment.

It would seem that the brain signals the eyes, "Keep on the lookout. Keep wide open." From time to time the nerves of the eyes report back, "Eyelids wide open." Then the ideas of anxiety and wide-open eyelids become associated together in the brain.

Now, if you learn to allow your eye-lids to remain comfortably in a less fully open position, this will be reported to the brain, and this state of affairs is associated with an absence of anxiety. So, instead of being over-alert, the mind becomes calmer. Anxiety is reduced.

When about to commence practising the exercise, allow your eyelids to close, naturally and easily. The lids are just lightly touching each other. As you relax more completely, the eyelids part just a little so that they are no touching each other, and you become aware of a little chink of light. This is the fully relaxed position of the eyelids. You should aim for this.

Some people do not close their eyes before they commence to relax. They are just left open. As relaxation becomes more complete the lids close very slowly over a period of a few minutes. With this method, relaxation of the mind and a good degree of regression is obtained before the lids actually close.

Relaxing in discomfort. This is essential as you become more experienced in relaxing meditation. The aim is more complete relaxation of the mind.

You can practise in positions of varying discomfort according to your taste and the degree to which you have mastered the exercise. When you can do it well lying on the floor, try lying with a few pebbles under your back in the region of the shoulder blades. When you can do this, you are immediately aware of the much greater relaxation of mind, and soon notice that the relaxation remains with you for increasing periods in your everyday life.

In the sitting position you can put a small clip on the skin of your arm. You immediately relax deeply so as to avoid the feeling of discomfort. This soon passes off, and you come to feel a very complete relaxation of mind.

Young people can practice in the cross-legged position and maintain a sufficient degree of discomfort by pulling their legs under their buttocks as the yogis do.

Combining the exercise with activity. When you have mastered the technique, are familiar with the relaxed feeling of the mind, and have learned to induce it quite easily and quickly while sitting down, you have reached the stage when you can practise the exercise while actually doing things.

The first step is very simple. As you relax, you allow your eyes to open a little, and to close again very slowly. Do this in time with your breathing. As you breathe in, your eyes open, then they close again as you breathe out. All the time, maintain the deep relaxation of your mind. At first, you are content to have your eyes open just a little. As you become more experienced they can open wider and wider.

The next stage is to do your exercise as you walk slowly down the street. You feel the relaxation of your mind. You are conscious of the ease and rhythm of your body as you move; and all the time are aware of the relaxation of the muscles of the face and the calm of mind.

Similarly, the housewife can practise while doing rhythmical domestic tasks such as polishing or using the vacuum cleaner. The calm and ease of mind induced by the exercise is thus kept with patients in all the tasks of everyday life.

Relief Of Symptoms

Once you have mastered the relaxation of the body, the relaxation of the mind, and regression, you are in a position to use a more direct approach to the relief of anxiety symptoms and the promotion of better responses to life situations.

In its simplest form this consists of presenting to your mind very simple ideas for improvement while still in the relaxed and regressed state.

Helpful Trains Of Thought

The trains of thought which I have set out in relation to various symptoms are intended merely as a guide. Each individual will modify them according to his own needs.

If **apprehension** is a prominent symptom, as it often is, proceed with a train of thought like this:

Relaxed.
Whole of my body relaxed.
Relaxed and calm.
Calm all through me.
Calm in my face.
Calm in mind.

It is not just a matter of repeating these ideas over in your mind. Do it slowly, easily comfortably, and really **experience the feeling of each idea in turn.**

When **tension** predominates, use a train of thought like this:

Relaxed.
Whole body relaxed.
Relaxation in my arm.
Feel it in my mind.
Feel my mind relaxed.

Feel the relaxation in your arm; then feel this relaxation of your arm in your mind. Be sure that you are doing it properly. Feel in your mind the relaxation that is in your arm.

In all exercise make sure that you **maintain relaxation of the face muscles** because of their effect on mental relaxation.

Relaxed.
Legs, arms, whole body relaxed.
It is in my face.
Jaw muscles loose.
Muscles around the eyes are relaxed.
Whole face smoothes out.
Forehead relaxed - deeply.
I feel it in my mind.

Relaxation is the natural way to peace of mind. Many want to overcome their nervous trouble through their own resources. They do not want to rely on taking sedatives and tranquillisers over a long period.

Relaxed.
Natural to relax.
It is the natural way.
To rest, and relax, and be calm.
Natural way to gather strength.
Strength of body, and calm of mind.

Of course, this sequence of thought is absolutely true. Relaxation is nature's way of coping with tension and anxiety.

Emphasis on feeling that it is good. When suffering from anxiety and chronic nervous tension, it is easy to feel that nothing seems good any more. The lustre goes from life. Things that once brought pleasure no longer do so. There may come a sensation of emptiness and destitution. But you can relax and help yourself along these lines:

Relaxed.
Good to relax.
Feel the relaxation all through me.

Good to feel it like that.
Really good.
Wonderful feeling.
Soon you find your outlook is changing, and once more things in ordinary life begin to feel good.

Experience the letting go feeling. Anxiety and nervous tension often make people restricted. They cannot let themselves go. This affects their work, leisure hours, and intimate life. They can help themselves thus:

Relaxed.
I feel the relaxation.
Feel the muscles let go.
They let go all through me.
It is in my mind.
I let go.

Feeling of inner strength. The effects of anxiety tend to destroy morale. You may have had the condition a long time and had treatment that has not helped. You feel like giving in. But you can be promised at least some help from the practice of the Relaxing Mental Exercise. So do not give up. When you are thoroughly relaxed, think along these lines:

Relaxed.
All muscles relaxed.
The calm of it all through me.
I feel the calm and the ease.
The calm that gives me strength.
The inner strength.
I feel the inner strength.

Remember the importance of the prior relaxation and regression.

Developing self-discipline. The way back to health from nervous illness always demands a fair degree of self-discipline. Some conditions require more, some less; and some patients find self-discipline easier than others. But all need it for the struggle ahead. They can help themselves like this:

Relaxed.
Relaxed and calm.
The calm that gives us the strength.
The inner strength.
The strength to do what we have to do.

They can proceed further along these lines:

The inner strength.
It is calm strength.
Easy strength.
Easier and easier to be strong.
At first self discipline is difficult, very difficult. But with practice it becomes easier and easier.

Relief Of Particular Symptoms

Insomnia. Some degree of sleeplessness is a fairly constant feature of anxiety conditions. The main problem is that insomnia is such a disturbing symptom that people turn to sleeping tablets far too quickly. Most people can learn to use the following relaxing technique to put themselves to sleep. I have recently been treating a doctor with chronic anxiety who had been taking sleeping capsules every night for 25 years. He learned the relaxing method of putting himself to sleep in 3 or 4 sessions, and since then has taken no sedative at night at all. But it does not come quite as easily as this to everyone. Give yourself a little time to get into the swing of it, and be patient when it does not all come at once.

When you have mastered Relaxing Mental Exercise, it is quite a simple matter to put yourself to sleep. You will have been practising the exercise in relatively uncomfortable positions. Now do them when you go to bed, and with the added warmth and comfort they will seem very easy indeed.

Relaxed.
Legs are relaxed.
Utterly relaxed.
All I feel of them is their weight on the bed.
Heavy relaxation.
Heavy drowsy relaxation.
It comes all through me.
Heavy, drowsy, sleepy.
My body is heavy with it.
It is in my face.
Eyelids are heavy with it.
So drowsy, so sleepy.
It is all through me.
When you really feel the heaviness, and the sleepiness, and weight in your eyelids, you just turn over on to your side into a

sleeping position and you are asleep.

If you wake during the night, you just repeat the same procedure. It is important to do it systematically and in a relaxed fashion. Do not allow yourself to get restless or irritable with yourself. Do it systematically and you will be off to sleep again.

This approach is effective not only with insomnia caused by anxiety but with insomnia resulting from almost any cause.

Phobias. Relaxing Mental Exercise can be used in 3 ways in the self-management of phobias. **First**, practise them when you are not in the phobic situation. Let us suppose you have a phobia about going outside – you practise at home when there is no particular occasion to go outside. Do the exercise – very relaxed and letting yourself regress – and think:

Relaxed.
Whole body relaxed.
Relaxed and calm and easy in myself.
Easy in myself.
Easy in myself wherever I go.

The exercise is repeated quietly and easily several times a day.

The **second** way is slightly different. As you relax, visualise yourself at ease in the phobic situation. In the present example it means seeing yourself in the street, quite relaxed and comfortable. Do it very completely. As you relax more thoroughly, you see yourself with greater and greater vividness. You are aware that you are calm and comfortable, and all the time that you visualise yourself in this way you are relaxed and at ease in yourself.

Relaxed.
Utterly calm and easy.
See myself go out the door.
I am calm and easy.
Down the street.
I can see myself.
Calm and easy.
Nothing disturbs me.

In the **third method**, you bring yourself closer and closer to the centre of the phobic situation. You go to the door. As you do so, pause, and capture again the relaxed feeling in your mind which you experience during the exercise. Go outside, relaxed and easy, and then return, Repeatedly venture to the edge of the phobic situation. If you experience the slightest feeling of anxiety, consciously recapture the relaxed feeling of the exercise. Do it easily. No panic. Do it little by little, more and more each day. The secret is that you do not allow anxiety to develop. Because of this, the conditioning process allows you to go further each day. Soon you are rewarded by finding you are at ease in the phobic situation. But remember, this takes time and self discipline.

On the one hand, you must make yourself do it; on the other, you must not push yourself so far that your become anxious.

The success of this approach depends entirely upon using the regression which comes with relaxation. I believe that to overcome a phobia by self-discipline in cold blood is almost impossible.

Speech difficulty. Those who have difficulty with speech can use Relaxing Mental Exercise to gain greater fluency. Those who stutter, and who are tense when speaking, can be helped because the practice of the exercise lowers the general level of anxiety. Tension is reduced and the words come more easily.

They can also incorporate Relaxing Mental Exercise into their speech therapy. They practise the exercise, and while still completely relaxed in both body and mind count aloud – slowly , easily clearly – and all the time maintain relaxation of body and mind. In the same way reading and reciting can be practised.

Speaking on the telephone is often a major problem for those who stutter. This situation is very well suited for help from mental exercise. As you take up the receiver, close your eyelids and relax completely. You are leisurely, and take your time before replying, and you feel the relaxation through the whole of your being.

If real stuttering is associated with anxiety and nervous tension it can be helped by this approach. On the other hand, if you should be one of those who stutter in the absence of anxiety, it is better to seek help through orthodox speech therapy.

Asthma. I have seen many people completely relieved of asthma following treatment by relaxation and regression. I have seen many others who, although not completely relieved, have vastly improved.

I really believe that if you suffer from asthma you cannot afford not to take treatment by Relaxing Mental Exercise. But remember: do not expect too much too quickly.

It is important to practice Relaxing Mental Exercise

conscientiously in the period between the attacks when your breathing is relatively free and easy. Do not wait until you get an attack – it is then often difficult to attain the relaxation and regression. The greatest benefit comes from doing the exercise when you are free of asthma. Possible future attacks are warded off and reduced in severity. If you should suffer an attack after starting the exercise, do not be discouraged. The relief of the asthma is usually a gradual process.

Relaxing Mental Exercise is effective in two ways. The exercise reduces the level of anxiety, and reduce the tendency to overreact to stress. Patients can also use the exercise in a more direct way. As they do them, they should let the idea of ease come to the mind – ease of body, ease of breathing.

Relaxed.
All my muscles relaxed.
Feel the relaxation and the ease.
The ease of it all through me.
The ease of it in my face, in my mind,
in my breathing.
Ease in my breathing.
Breathing easily.

When starting the exercise, it is wise to continue with your usual asthma medication. Reduce it only when you have got into the way of doing the exercise easily and effectively. Then reduce it slowly. This is best done in co-operation with your doctor.

Nervous rashes. In general, nervous rashes are distinguished by the way in which the condition of the skin waxes and wanes with the emotional state. Relaxing Mental Exercise lead to a calmer state of mind in which the patient feels less frustrated by the various stresses of his life situation. The rash improves. It often happens that the rash subsides and drugs previously used can be dropped. To avoid a relapse, it is wise to continue the exercise.

Examples Of Other Benefits

Smoking. If you yourself wish to stop smoking, I would advise you to go about it this way. Set yourself a deadline, some day about two weeks hence, which is to be the day on which you will stop. It is good to make it the weekend or some day when you will have reasonable leisure. In the two weeks learn to do the exercise properly– very completely.

When you have mastered the physical and mental relaxation, and can let yourself regress a little, you can present ideas to your mind. Smoking. Silly habit. Dirty habit. All that stuff in your lungs. Unnatural. Nasty. Tastes nasty. Smells nasty. Then, on the morning of the allotted day, throw away your cigarettes. And that is the end of it.

Let us be quite clear about this. The basic difficulty in giving up smoking is that you feel you want a cigarette, and if you do not have one you become tense. When you have mastered the exercise, you can control your tension, and it becomes relatively easy just not to have another cigarette.

Nail biting. A 27 year old man sought help to stop biting his nails. He said he had the habit ever since he could remember. He was extraordinarily tense, and he said he did most of his nail-biting when he was worried and on edge. He admitted that he was so tense that with little provocation he would flare up. He did the exercise, and when last seen, about six weeks after his first visit, claimed that he had mastered the habit. I saw that his nails were beginning to grow normally.

Blushing. About two years ago an attractive nurse said she had been plagued with blushing for as long as she could remember. She blushed in the company of young men. She blushed in buses, and did not even like asking other nurses about patients on account of her blushing. She learned the exercise, but I was not sure how much help she had gained until she came in a few weeks ago to ask advice about some other problem. When I asked her about the blushing she merely commented, "Oh, that's all gone," as if she had forgotten all about it.

Fringe benefits. A patient who seeks help on account of tension in the home, and masters the exercise, finds that he is easier at his work and can do it more effectively. Many a wife has said that her husband is easier to live with, although this was not the cause of him coming to see me. As the level of anxiety is reduced, sleep improves. This is a very consistent finding of those who do the exercise. Many people have told me how their golf has improved. When they are less tense they naturally swing more freely.

Patients who ski have told me that their turns have improved because they are less tense and can balance better with more

\ythm. The numerous benefits are discussed further in

This is the end of the first half of **RWD.**

Summary [102]

General Principles
1. Don't be put off by the simplicity.
2. It is natural and that is why it is so successful.
3. It is effective irrespective of the cause of anxiety
4. Don't expect too much too quickly.
5. Be prepared for ups and some downs.
6. Remember that it does not all come at once.
7. Don't be impatient when at first you cannot relax - if you could there would be no need for detailed instructions.

The Relaxing Mental Exercise
8. Bring yourself to like the Relaxing Mental Exercise.
9. Physical relaxation is a key to mental relaxation.
10. Use a symmetrical posture (eg sit, lay down or squat).
11. Posture should not be too comfortable.
    (so the relaxation comes from the mind itself).
12. If you tend to fall asleep use a more uncomfortable posture.
13. Fit the exercise into your routine eg before leaving for work and later on in the day. About 10 minutes twice a day.
14. Keep the feeling of relaxation during everyday tasks.
15. See over page for the main RWD train of thought edited to fit on 1 page.

---

102 Paraphrasing Meares words from **RWD**

Main RWD Train Of Thought On 1 Page[103]

1. Do not just say prompts over and over or repeat the thoughts.
2. Don't think about the prompts in critical logical fashion as this stops the mind from slowing and temporarily regressing.
3. Just present each prompt to the mind and experience the appropriate feeling.

It is good to relax.	*Feel it there deeply.*
Relaxing is natural.	*Feel it all thru.*
The natural way to calm & ease.	*In my face.*
Think of the legs,	*Feel the relaxation & the calm*
the muscles of the legs.	*The relaxation is all thru me,*
Allow them to let go.	*& so is the calm that goes with it.*
Feel them relax, really feel it.	*The calm of it is part of me.*
Muscles of the legs let go.	*It is all thru me*
They let go so all we feel is the	*in my body & my mind.*
weight of them on the floor.	*Feel the calm all thru.*
Heavy & comfortable.	*Feel it in my body.*
The natural weight of the legs.	*Feel it in my mind.*
Feel this easy relaxation all thru.	*The calm pervades me.*
Feel it in the body.	*Let myself go.*
Arms are heavy - so relaxed.	*Let go & drift.*
Feel the weight of them.	*Drift in the calm of it.*
The natural weight.	*Just letting go,*
Natural to let oneself relax,	*Drift more & more.*
the mind learns to be calm	*Let me go with it.*
and to be at ease again.	*Let myself go*
Feel the relaxation more & more.	*more & more completely.*
It grows.	*Let go of myself,*
My whole body is relaxed.	*more & still more completely.*
Feel myself sitting in the chair.	
Sinking into the chair.	*[Gently let go into quietness]*
Feel it in the face.	
muscles of my face relax.	Unwanted thoughts can be stilled by
jaw is loose.	feeling ease of body, hands and face.
It is so relaxed,	
so loose that the lips part.	Finish after 10-15 mins:
Feel it in muscles around the eyes	Feel the relaxation. Remind yourself it is
Feel muscles of face smooth out.	good. Rest for a couple of minutes. If you
It is in the forehead.	feel drowsy or glassy eyed some extra
At the sides of my forehead,	rest will help re-balance before moving
	on to your next task.

---

103 Edited to fit on one page. Finish added.

2.5 Some Notes About Pain

Background

For people with pain Meares[104] suggested practising the Relaxing Mental Exercise for 10 mins, 3-4 times a day for several weeks, and then daily. Such people having become familiar with it will then be able to make good use of these **Notes**.

Pain serves as a warning - always be quite clear about what is causing pain before relieving it. Knowing the cause will help identify the correct action (eg remedy, rest, Relaxing Mental Exercise etc).

Introduction

You can learn to control pain in much the same way as tension and anxiety, and this includes pain from organic as well as psychological causes.

Pain serves as a warning of bodily harm but it may still seem too severe or too prolonged a warning. There is a reason for this, too. For example: You burn you hand. The pain is sudden, intense, severe, and immediately, automatically, you withdraw your hand from the flame. The pain caused this withdrawal to protect the hand from further injury. But the pain persists – so intensely that you cannot bear to touch the burn. This is again protective. By not touching, you avoid infection of the raw burn.

Of course, it is excessive pain that we desire to control. Many different factors may combine to make pain excessive. Some are organic (it depends what nerves are concerned, e.g., an abscess near a rigid tissue, such as the apex of a tooth, causes more pain than a similar infection near a soft tissue, such as under the skin); others are psychological and depend on general mental health, and constitutional factors also come into it – some people are undoubtedly more sensitive to pain than others.

If pain is coupled with distress, it quickly becomes excessive. The presence of a mild psychological depression makes the pain from some organic cause more severe and tends to make it persist after the organic cause has been removed. In fact, unrecognised depressive illness is one of the commonest causes of persistent pain for which no adequate organic cause can be found. It is important to consult your doctor if pain is associated with mental depression, with a tendency to be tearful, or difficulty

104 4th World Congress Psychiatry, 1966; Med J Aust Jan7: 11-12. 1967.

in getting started at every-day tasks.

Organic and functional pain. Pain arising from bodily injury is organic pain. Pain arising from psychological mechanisms within the mind is functional pain. And make no mistake, it is not imaginary but may be very severe. But the two should not be pigeon-holed as being always separate. Organic pain can cause the patient to worry, and this soon produces a psychological reaction, so the organic pain has a functional overlay.

Organic pain from psychological causes. When people are tense in the mind, they unconsciously hold their muscles tensely. When driving a car, for instance, a person may come to feel pain in the neck and shoulders. It is organic pain, yet the prime cause is psychological – the tenseness of mind.

Pain And Distress

In ordinary circumstances pain hurts because the person reacts to it. Thus pain is rarely experienced in pure form.

You may find some of these ideas a little hard to accept at first. But this particular idea is basic to the management of pain, so please go along with me.

You can prove it easily enough. Stick a pin lightly in your forearm. It hurts. You screw up your face and perhaps say "ow" under your breath. You have reacted. But now decide that you will stick the pin in again, but this time you will not react to it in any way. Make sure your face muscles are calm and easy. Now stick in the pin as before. Yes, you feel it. But this time there is no hurt.

There is little or no hurt, provided you do not react to the painful stimulus. The sensation you do feel will give you the concept of pain in pure form.

It must be concluded that pain is not an unbearable sensation, provided the person does not react to it. This is true of much more severe pain than a pin prick.

Aggravation of pain by distress. The little boy is playing. He falls and skins his knees. He screams. In an instant his whole being is over-whelmed with pain. Mother lifts him up and holds him to her, kissing him on the cheeks. In a moment his distress is calmed and the pain passes, the sobbing dies down and he inquires about the toy he was playing with. Mother has quieted his distress, and the pain does not disturb him unduly. Remember that this comes about by her kissing his cheeks rather than attending to the injured knees.

Adults also react to pain with distress. One woman in childbirth may scream when she experiences pain, giving full vent to her distress. Another woman lies there silent, but tense and blanched, in obvious distress. A third woman may be led to relax in her mind. Then there is no distress. And because there is none, there is little discomfort.

Control of distress. This, then is a basic rule: Whatever happens, I shall not allow myself to be overwhelmed by distress.

Distress is a psychological reaction. It is possible to influence and control it by an act of mind, if one sets about it the right way.

Many people do it simply through the natural intuitive processes of the mind; others can learn to do it by following these ideas, going along with them, and by experiencing the calm and ease of the mental exercise already described.

Fear is one of the other factors that can also increase the level of anxiety, increase tension, and increase pain. Pain that is too prolonged, when associated with distress, guilt, and fear, soon tends to destroy morale. Anything that controls pain will not only boost morale but will have an indirect effect on physical healing.

Reactions to pain. Some primitive peoples cope with the pain of severe injury better than the more civilised and sophisticated Western peoples. This idea is quite important in the self-management of pain because it makes people realise they are not attempting something new and difficult, but are merely relearning how to use the ability to control excessive pain.

Some people react to pain with hostility and are angry about it - "Why should this happen to me?" the result is increased tension and increased perception of pain.

Others have a depressive reaction – "I am like this because of what I have done." They associate their pain with punishment for some past wrongdoing for which they feel guilt. They need to accept pain for what it is – a warning of injury.

But the philosophical reaction to pain is the one to be aimed for. "It can't be helped. I shall get over it." A person free of pain can see this is the only sensible and mature way to respond. But when the pain is upon him, it is not so easy.

Approaches To Functional Pain

Understand the cause. It is clear that the first step in self management is the acceptance of the idea that the pain is, in fact, the result of anxiety.

Reduce the anxiety. If the cause is some conflict that you are aware of, anxiety and pain can be reduced by facing up to the problem realistically. Another way to reduce anxiety is by experience. Reduction of anxiety makes people less sensitive to pain.

Increasing your pain threshold. If you gently pinch your skin, you feel it, but it does not hurt. If you pinch it harder, you come to the stage when it does hurt. This is your threshold of pain in these particular circumstances.

The threshold of pain is quite variable. If you get another person to pinch you, and at the same time consciously relax, he can pinch much harder before you feel pain. Similarly if he distracts your attention, you do not feel the pain so readily.

But if he makes a show of what he is going to do, pain comes more readily, because he has mobilised your anxiety, and this lowers the pain threshold.

Relaxing Mental Exercise is used to increase the pain threshold in two ways: First, the reduction of anxiety makes you less sensitive to pain; and secondly, they can condition you against being disturbed by painful stimuli. This applies to either functional or organic pain.

Approaches To Organic Pain

People's attitudes vary, largely according to personality.

Enduring the pain. "The pain is there. I have got it. That is all there is to it." This is an attitude of a rather stoic and well integrated personality. The disadvantage is nothing is done to alleviate the pain. But in as much as there is no reaction of distress, guilt, or fear, the pain is made no worse.

Denial of pain. This is quite a good way of psychologically protecting yourself. Friends are told, "No, it is not hurting at all." This makes it easier to deny the pain to yourself and has a kind of primitive magic– saying something to make it come true. Denial helps to control pain, but it is seldom complete. But it does hold off the destructive influences of distress, fear and guilt.

Distraction. This gains respite from pain. The patient with arthritis says, "I am better when doing something. I am really better at work; the pain does not worry me so much then." People

ching TV or going to a show.

ulty, of course, is that the brain gives high priority for

ain of any severity, so it usually takes something of

urgency to divert attention. (An injured footballer may finish the game before he is aware of the extent of his injury.)

Auto-suggestion. People often use this quite naturally. They make themselves think, "I am a little better this morning." This helps, but auto-suggestion is more effective if combined with the relaxing exercise. Used wisely, auto-suggestion is very valuable.

Feel the pain in its pure form. This is the best method of all. You accept pain for what it is – a warning. But accept it in its pure form without any overlay or embellishment. You soon learn that pain – that is, pure pain- really does not hurt.

Auto-suggestion carries a possible side effect of increasing suggestibility. Dissociation of the mind from pain (e.g., through hypnosis) is essentially a disintegrating process of the mind. Self management by feeling pain in its pure form works for greater integration and maturity of the personality.

Self Management Of Pain

Let us bring together in concise form some of the matters already discussed. You will then be quite clear in your mind as to what self-management of pain involves. You will see that there are 6 general principles and that success requires attention to each. The application of each of these principles is easy enough to master if you will just let yourself go along with the idea of it.

1. **Reduce the general level of anxiety.** This is the first principle in the self-management of pain. It is essential, as anxiety increases pain. The reduction of anxiety is achieved by understanding the nature of pain, by facing up to and resolving conflicts which have been causing anxiety, and by Relaxing Mental Exercise.

2. **Avoid psychological reactions that increase pain.** This principle means that, whatever happens, you will not allow yourself to be overwhelmed by distress, which is so easily induced by pain. You will be realistic if the pain should lead you into guilty thoughts about past shortcomings.

You will halt the feeling of fear which would only make you feel pain more acutely. In each of these matters the calm engendered by the Relaxing Mental Exercise helps.

3. **Use psychological reactions that reduce pain.** According to circumstances, and your individual personality, you can use various psychological reactions to reduce pain. You can deny it and use various distractions to forget it. If your personality is such that you can do it, you can dissociate yourself from the pain and stand apart from it. All can practise auto-suggestion, and most can get some help from it provided it is done in a really relaxed state of mind.

4. **Practice the experience.** This, of course, forms the basis of this approach to the self management of pain. It allays anxiety, wards of distress, allows the effective use of auto-suggestion, and of itself reduces the threshold of pain.

5. **Condition against pain.** Conditioning becomes possible through the calm state of mind induced by the exercise. You subject yourself to minor painful stimuli. You are not disturbed. Gradually use more severe stimuli; you maintain calm of mind and are still not disturbed. In a little while you can tolerate quite severe stimuli without discomfort. By the process of conditioning, you come to be less disturbed by pain in general.

6. **Accept pain in pure form.** This last principle follows quite naturally from the practice of the other principles. When you have mastered these, you will come to realise the fundamental truth– **pure pain does not hurt.**

Managing Different Kinds Of Pain

Chronic pain. Follow the 6 principles already outlined.

Pain you are expecting. One of the difficulties is that you tend to become anxious. Your anxiety shows itself in tension of both body and mind, and as a result you feel the pain more intensely.

But now you have practised the Relaxing Mental Exercise, the situation is different. When you know that something painful is going to happen, you simply relax. This not only prevents the pain being made worse by anxiety but allows you to experience the pain in pure form so that you are not distressed or hurt by it. In general, pain that we are able to anticipate is quite easy to control by this system of self-management.

Sudden, unexpected pain. This is a different clinical problem again. The difficulty is that it is easy to be overcome with distress before you can compose yourself. It happens in the case of an unexpected blow, a broken bone, a burn, etc.

These studies in the self-management of pain help in two ways. If you have learned something of the approach and have had some experience in the Relaxing Mental Exercise, you do not react so drastically to sudden pain. This has been my own experience, and a number of patients have volunteered a similar observation.

Secondly, you now have the means to bring yourself quickly under control and restore your composure.

Summary

General Principles
1. Pain serves as a warning - be quite clear what is causing the pain before relieving it.
2. You can learn to control excessive hurt in the same way as tension and anxiety.

The Relaxing Mental Exercise
3. Practice for 10 mins, 3-4 times a day for several weeks and then 10 mins twice a day.
4. During the Exercise you relax through slight discomfort (and gradually more challenging stimuli). You are not disturbed. You come to be less disturbed by pain in general.
5. Practising the Exercise allays anxiety, wards off distress, allows auto-suggestion, and of itself reduces the threshold of pain.

Managing Pain
6. Accept the warning but, accept pain in its pure form. Pure pain does not hurt.
7. Other reactions you can use: Deny pain. Use distractions to forget it. Some can dissociate and stand apart from it.
8. If you are about to experience pain or it has commenced:
   - You simply relax.
   - Don't allow yourself to be overwhelmed by distress
   - Be realistic if pain should lead to guilty thoughts
   - Halt fear which would increase the feeling of pain.
9. If pain is unexpected the Exercise will help you not react as much to potential distress. You use the calm to bring yourself quickly under control and restore your composure.

The End

3. Stillness Meditation

The Fine Tuning Of The Relaxing Mental Exercise after RWD

3.1 Introduction

Meares[105] succinctly outlines his **RWD** program: *"...we have within our minds a self-regulating mechanism which, if given a chance, can control nervous tension... It is a matter of providing favourable circumstances... This is attained in five simple steps.*

The first is to learn how to relax our body very completely. This is simple physical relaxation.

The second step is to learn to experience the physical relaxation . It is not just our body being very relaxed. It is the experience of the relaxation in our whole self, our mind, our whole being.

The third step is to practise this experience of relaxation in circumstances of minor discomfort, so that the relaxation transcends the discomfort. This is very important.

The fourth step is to practise this simple mental exercise for 10 minutes a couple of times a day.

And the last step is to let this ease of mind come into our daily life..."

A person who practices the Relaxing Mental Exercise for 10 minutes twice a day and lets the effortless ease into daily life will reap many benefits. **After RWD**, Meares fine tuned his Relaxing Mental Exercise and it became Stillness Meditation. They are essentially the same process leading to the same natural mental state except Stillness Meditation is simpler and more direct.

Meares' background was agriculture and medical science. Pauline McKinnon (s1.12) trained as a professional singer and went on to live a full life until she was crippled by agoraphobia. She saw Meares around 1974, at the start of the Stillness Meditation period, and daily practice eventually led to her complete recovery. In her writings (1983 onward), McKinnon uses her own plain language to express the same ideas as Meares. Section 3 outlines Meares' method from later publications[106] and adopts some of McKinnon's plain language[107]. Sources are only footnoted for critical specifics and quotes.

After RWD, Meares wrote about the process of Stillness Meditation, transcending discomfort, making the stillness more general and encouraging the flow on of calm into daily life or *"learning the calm, experiencing the calm and, ultimately, living the*

---

105 Proceedings Medico-Legal Soc Vic V12:277-284 1973

106 The Wealth Within, Life Without Stress, A Better Life, Am J Clin Hypnosis 25(2-3):114-121 1983, Aust Fam Physician 1976: amongst others.

107 McKinnon P, Living Calm in a Busy World; In Stillness Conquer Fear

calm"[108].

Section 3 also showcases Meares' trains of thought to illustrate how they evolved into the simple prompts used in Stillness Meditation.

There are 3 key concepts:

A Natural Self Regulatory Mechanism. Within our minds is a self regulating mechanism which can reduce nervous tension. This mechanism is a natural part of every human. It is already there. The "know how" is built into all of us (but some may have temporarily forgotten). It is a matter of providing favourable circumstances for the mind to work this way.

Stillness Meditation Is Natural Mental Rest[109] The stillness of mind is more than "meditation"! It is natural mental rest. It is a way of allowing our mind to re-learn again to be calm and at ease as nature intended. Generally, 20-45 mins split over 2-3 sessions per day is sufficient. Meares' Stillness Meditation for this duration permits the mental rest nature intended humans to experience each day (but may not occur without Stillness Meditation).

Living Calm. This is the flow on of calm into daily life. The effects of Stillness Meditation persist and flow onwards for a time afterwards. Effortlessness (or ease) and calm are the main features of the flow on. This flow on of effortless calm can be carried over so it transfers into everyday life. It is learning to live calm - Living Calm[110].

This onward flow of calmness is not the same as the meditative state. It does not involve persistence of the meditative state. It is not a drowsy trance or some such. Rather, it is a deep seated change characterised by calm and ease as the person, in normal consciousness and not meditating, goes about doing things. It gradually enhances the ability to do even difficult things calmly (and easily)[111]. Meares also referred to this as the Discipline of Ease.

Stillness Meditation is a means to an end. It is not an end of itself. It is the effects of Stillness Meditation - living calm – that is the most important thing. Meares wrote that we do not live to meditate. Stillness Meditation is a means of learning to live calm. The mental rest of Stillness Meditation is extremely helpful. Learning to live calm is the other half of the equation. It is learning to live the better quality of life nature intended.

---

108 McKinnon P, Living Calm in a Busy World, p84
109 P. McKinnon's term for mental homeostasis via atavistic regression.
110 Living Calm in a Busy World is also title of book by P. McKinnon
111 The Wealth Within eg p23, 34-36, 46, 63 & Pt 2; The Silver Years, pp94-96

3.2 A Natural Self Regulatory Mechanism[112]

Mental Stillness Is Natural

In the old way of our prehistoric primitive ancestors, there was no work or exercise but only hunting and plant gathering interspersed with periods of mental and physical rest. In our modern life way, we are accustomed to doing exercise instead of the physical activity of hunting and gathering. If we want to be fit in the body for our health or for sports performance we train for it. We think it natural that we should do physical exercise at the gym, pool or on the track. If we want to be fit in mind it is equally natural that we should practise the relaxing exercise of Stillness Meditation. This is the attitude in which we should approach the idea, as Stillness Meditation is perfectly natural. It is lack of physical exercise and lack of natural mental rest, that we call Stillness Meditation, that is unnatural.

Our mind developed from the simplicity of the prehistoric primitive into the complexity of modern human. But, our mind can still slip back into more primitive modes of function. This is atavistic regression: Meares' medical term for Stillness Meditation. Atavistic regression is the process in which our mind temporarily goes back to a far simpler ancestral mode. Towards that of our primitive ancestors with its simple functioning and lack of complex thinking. This temporary regression occurs quite naturally in healthy people when they let their mind go off guard in day dreaming and reverie. Some people describe this as going "blank". Afterwards, they recall being awake and in the moment but not really thinking or doing anything at all. In this temporary state, the mind wanders uncontrolled by logic. It has slipped back to a far simpler and more primitive mode of function.

Anxiety is produced when nerve signals arriving at the brain cannot be properly sorted out and integrated. Anxiety is lessened if the quantity of nerve signals arising from worry and from physical stimuli is reduced. This happens when we are on holidays and the tension of anxiety is replaced by relaxation and ease of mind.

Anxiety is also reduced by things that help integration of nerve signals eg. certain prescription drugs and ordinary sleep. Deep mental relaxation (Stillness Meditation) works like sleep only it is far more effective. The regression of deep mental relaxation enhances the

---

112 The Wealth Within Pt3; Management of the Anxious Patient; A Better Life, pp127-130

integration of nerve signals.

Anxiety evolved in fairly recent times as it depends upon complex functions of the mind. Animals experience fear but not true anxiety. The situation for prehistoric primitives must have been similar. The mind that regresses goes back to a very primitive way of functioning. This old way does not know anxiety! This is what happens in deep mental relaxation. It is the same in reverie and day dreaming. In these moments, we feel a deep mental relaxation because our mind has regressed to this anxiety free state. When we practice deep mental relaxation, our mind goes into this anxiety free state. It is thus able to start off again with new anxiety free patterns of functioning. Afterwards, we know of this calm clear tranquillity as it persists or flows on for a period of time. There is an onwards flow of these anxiety free patterns of functioning that can be cultivated or enhanced.

Mental relaxation is nature's way of dealing with anxiety. We all have within us this self regulatory mechanism. It is already there. This mechanism is a part of each of us that nature intended to function so that we might flourish. In the practice of Stillness Meditation we re-awaken the functioning of this mechanism. By putting time aside to practice this relaxing experience we ensure we get adequate mental rest. It is a bit like going to bed to get adequate sleep every night.

The Numerous Benefits

Meares' descriptions[113] of the numerous benefits of Stillness Meditation and the flow on of calm could fill a book. In summary, they are:

- Greater ease of mind.
- Relief from psychosomatic symptoms.
- Absence of disturbing dreams.
- Improved sleep (and a way to rest when events curtail sleep).
- Significant relief from pain
- Improved general health (eg. reduced cortisol, improved immune system etc).
- Edges and distortions of personality smoothed out– the shy become less timid, the aggressive become more passive, the outgoing more inward looking, the overly dramatic more real and so on. Balance is the theme.
- Being more creative, clearer thinking and having better judgement.
- Better interpersonal relationships.
- Better sexual relationships due to less tension.

---

113 The Wealth Within, Pt2; A Better Life, pp 131-137

- Increased work capacity.
- Smoother physical movements and reactions including better sport performance.
- Inner peace and some kind of philosophical understanding of life – Meares wrote that after you have practised for a while you too will know what he meant.

Significant Relief From Pain

Some further comment on "significant relief from pain" seems warranted. At some time in our lives we shall all be faced with pain.

If we have mastered Stillness Meditation and are then confronted with pain we can use our minds in a way that will transcend it.[114] It is a matter of learning to use this pain controlling ability which is latent within us. Stillness Meditation helps management of pain in several ways: [115] [116]

- It reduces the general level of anxiety,
- It allays anxiety about pain and wards off distress and fear,
- The use of progressively challenging stimuli after learning the basics of Stillness Meditation builds up tolerance and this allows less disturbance by pain in general (refer S3 **Making The Stillness More General,** footnote 117 also contains further information)
- It increases the threshold of pain.

In summary, Meares' Stillness Meditation facilitates the development of a pattern for the perception of pain in simple form - pure pain - pain that does not hurt.

114 Why be Old, p218
115 Amer J Clin Hypnosis 11(1):55-57. 1968
116 The Wealth Within, pp52-63

3.3 Natural Mental Rest

Daily Practice

Meares emphasised that many people were unaware that they carry a significant level of anxiety and tension. It is their experience of life and to them it seems normal. When this tension is relieved they realise things can be better. This takes a little time. Some day to day variation in Stillness Meditation is normal. Some day to day fluctuation in the general level of anxiety is also normal. Meares said that people starting out on the practice of Stillness Meditation will have good days and days that are not so good. If you improve for a few days, and then have a not-so good day, do not be put off. Expect change. But, don't expect too much too quickly. Meares also emphasised the importance of practising every day, as this tended to ward off or blunt the not-so good ones.

Meares often used to see "general" patients weekly for 2-3 months and they were advised to practice every day between visits. As the visits became less frequent whether that took 2-3 months or longer, they were advised to keep meditating.

Some people see Stillness Meditation like a prescription taken till you are "fixed up" and then stop. Meares' recommended meditating on a daily basis for the rest of your life. Remembering that time spent in stillness provides the natural mental rest which came to wild humans spontaneously. In modern times, work, computers and other things can get in the way. Daily Stillness Meditation helps ensure you get sufficient daily mental rest.

Meares himself after he had practised for nearly 3 decades said that he still felt that Stillness Meditation was doing him good and his practice was improving - every day. But, he noticed a long term beneficial effect and an improvement more on some days than others. Some practice sessions were better than others with a stronger flow of calm through the rest of those days. He hoped that he might come to meditate still better.

How Long To Be Still For

In **RWD**, people were said to need about 10 mins, twice a day. Later, Meares fine tuned these numbers (see Table 1 & 2). These and other estimates[117] indicate a ballpark of 20-45 mins split over 2-3 sessions a day. This being suitable for helping symptoms of anxiety, anxiety related illness, phobias and for personal development.

First, learn the regular habit of meditating 2-3 times a day for 10

---

117 McKinnon P, Living Calm in a Busy World, p232

minutes or so each session. Once you have some experience in Stillness Meditation then you may fine tune the length of your total meditation time within the 20-45 mins daily and remember *"the thing that really counts is how we let the effects of our mental ataraxis into our daily life"*.[118] Meditating so as to live calm.

Table 1. General Recommendations

Year	Group	Session (mins)	Sessions per day	Total (mins)	Footnote
1967	General	10	2	20	[119]
1969	General	10	2 or 3	20-30	[120]
1978	Most	10	2	20	[121]
1978	Nearly All	10	2 or 3	20-30	**[122]**

Table 2. Recommendations for Specific Groups

Year	Group	Session (mins)	Sessions per day	Total (mins)	Footnote
1967	Pain	10	3 or 4	30-40	[123]
1969	Students	10	2 or 3	20-30	[124]
1986	Students	15	3 or 4	45-60	[125]
1981	Psychosomatic Illness	15	2	30	[126]

One Longer Session Each Week

Stillness Meditation class consists of a longer meditation session (45 mins approx). Class has several significant benefits eg a trusted teacher, a place that feels safe and the "calm of the crowd". At the

---

118 The Wealth Within, p46
119 Relief without Drugs
120 The Melbourne Age Newspaper, 7\5\1969
121 The Wealth Within, pX
122 The Wealth Within, p46
123 4ᵗʰ World Congress Psychiatry, 1966; Med J Aust Jan7: 11-12. 1967
124 Student Problems & a Guide to Study, p84
125 Life Without Stress, p48
126 The Healing Power of Meditation. Queensland Relaxation Centre. CD

start, the teacher will utter a train that will lapse into silence a
teacher will use gentle reassuring touch on head and shoulder:

People who are located remotely from a Meares' Stillness
Meditation teacher or class and have mastered the basics could
consider for a maximum of 1 day per week extending their practice to
30-45 mins. This corresponds to the total maximum duration of daily
mental rest recommended. Unless you have cancer, or an analagous
organic disease there is no good reason to exceed 45 mins duration in
a day (NB Meares would have raised concerns eg time lost to living).

Cancer [127]

Unless distance prevented it, Meares[128] saw his cancer patients
several times a week for a month and then less frequently– with the
patient practising for 10 minutes, 2-3 times per day and then building
up to the longer periods of up to 1-3 hours or more daily after they
had learnt his method and as their strength permitted it.

Meares reported that those using Stillness Meditation to help
heal cancer generally coped better, had pain relief and an improved
quality of life.[129] Stillness Meditation might be used in combination
with other therapies or by itself. But, it is the sick person who needs
to decide what is best for them with all the relevant information,
including well informed medical advice, at their fingertips.

Schizophrenia Or Similar Psychosis

Meares[130] wrote that a person at risk of schizophrenia etc should
only practice meditation under extremely close supervision as
meditation could aggravate that condition. However, he also added
that Stillness Meditation has prevented many sensitive apprehensive
sane persons from progressing to a worsened mental state: using
Stillness Meditation purely for anxiety reduction might steer such a
person away from that. But, for similar reasons, he believed that any
use of Stillness Meditation for mysticism should wait until the middle
years.[131]

Brain Injury, Disease And Mental Disability

Meares indicated that some people whose brains had been
damaged by injury or disease (eg circulatory or other disease) might

127 Meares used the term cancer in a general sense ie neoplasia. The advice in
this section is all Meares eg refer A Way of Doctoring including references.
128 Am J Clin Hypnosis 25(2-3):114-121. 1983
129 J Helen Vale Found V3(2):13-16. 1982; Aust Fam Physician 9(May):322-
325 ; Also The Silver Years p81-84
130 The Wealth Within p159-160
131 A Better Life, pp60-63

be unable to meditate. This might also apply to the severely mentally disabled who might only be able to learn simple relaxation[132]. If Stillness Meditation is beyond the ability of a brain damaged or disabled person the only option is to shift the goal posts to an "easier" form of meditation eg progressive relaxation, vague visualisation etc on the basis that something, even second best, is better than nothing.

Children [133] [134]

It is advantageous for children to learn of the naturalness of mental relaxation from an early age. The baby and later the growing child go through earlier stages of the evolution of the mind and this determines what can be taught. The relaxation habit can be taught early. At the lower end of primary school a simple form of dream like relaxation can be introduced. By the teenage years, Stillness Meditation can be introduced as a form of natural mental rest as a separate subject or as part of physical education where both physical and relaxing mental exercise are taught.

---

132 McKinnon, P, Living Calm in a Busy World, p121
133 A Better Life pp60-63
134 McKinnon, P. Living Calm in a Busy World in a Busy World pp150-180; Lets Be Still A Teaching Manual; Help Yourself & Your Child To Happiness

3.4 The Stillness Meditation Process

At The Beginning

"At the start we do not want to make things too difficult for ourselves"[135]

In Stillness Meditation class, generally speaking you will sit on a chair, at a set time, in the class room. But, what about your own daily practice? This could also be sitting or using static back (see p112).

In sitting, your head may rest on the back of the chair, your arms on your lap and your legs with knees bent and feet resting on the floor. If the chair has a low back that does not reach your head you will need to sit in an upright balanced position.

In your daily practice choose quiet familiar surroundings. Use the same posture each time. Pick times that permit regular daily practice to help get into the habit. You might start with 15 minutes twice a day and fine tune these times later. Use a (quiet) timer if you wish. Meares generally recommended a session in the morning after you had got up and woken up a bit and a second session later in the day eg during the afternoon.

The similarity of all these things make it easier. The same posture will provide a consistent amount of slight discomfort to relax through. Using relatively quiet familiar surroundings will involve less stimulation of the mind by extraneous stimuli. These things all help.

But they are not forever. Later on, after you have learnt the stillness, you gradually make changes in tiny steps to "broaden out" the same simple stillness experience. This is discussed later.

Relaxation Of Body, Mind And Self

Meares[136] wrote: *"The first thing we must learn is the physical relaxation of our body... We learn the physical relaxation of our body by the progressive relaxation of our muscles...*

...The next step is to **experience** *the physical relaxation of your body. It is not just our body being very relaxed. It is the experience of the relaxation in our whole self, our mind, our whole being...*

Strength training involves learning to try to contract muscles hard. Relaxation training is the reverse. It involves learning how to relax the muscles easily without effort. It is necessary to learn how to do this thoroughly so that you <u>let</u> relaxation occur. Remember, the muscles let go when they relax. The nerves communicate relaxation by sending fewer nerve impulses to the muscles. The contraction is

---

135 The Wealth Within, p46
136 A Better Life, pp106-126

reduced. Fewer impulses. Less effort. It really is effort-less.

However, even in deep relaxation there is still a small amount of contraction in certain muscles to hold posture - otherwise you would collapse like a jellyfish.

Learning the letting go feeling. When learning the sensations of physical relaxation, feel the relaxation, if need be shifting or lifting the limb or gently flexing muscles. Once, twice or more to help re-learn the feeling. You contract the muscles so you can then feel the letting go as the contraction releases. You contract and then relax a few times so that the feeling of relaxation becomes more and more a reality. You are learning the "letting go" and you only contract to contrast the feeling. You can make the contractions smaller and smaller until you find that you need not contract the muscles at all but can just feel the letting go.

If there is a secret, it is that the relaxing sensation is effortless as the nerve impulses to the muscle are fewer. So it really involves less effort. Fewer impulses. Less Effort. In this way it is a knack. However, undertanding the principles will help you get it quicker.

You can start at the toes and work up to the top: legs & feet, arms & hands, torso, face, jaw, eyes, face (again), forehead, sides of forehead. This sequence lets you work from the ground up to your head and face although letting each part relax is more important than any strict order.

Meares[137] mentions that some people may become tired and will do better to have a couple of sessions before they move onto the next stage of experiencing the end result of whole body (global) relaxation.

Generally speaking, in class you will remain in the same position seated on your chair. If you find it helps to contract and relax the muscles (ie with very tiny or no movement) you may do so a couple of times at the start of class. However, the class is about learning the letting go without movement. This is the way Meares taught and how it is taught in class today. It is expected that the student spend whatever time is needed on the above prelimnaries in their own practise (or sometimes, if necessary, with their teacher).

Simplify. Once you have learnt to relax the various muscles quickly and easily, you know how, and you can dispense with these preliminary contract - relax exercises. They were only to help you learn! So, you simplify the process and let go the tension in the limbs, the torso and then the head, face and forehead. Eventually, you will feel a wave or flow of relaxation a short time after you begin. It is this overall bodily relaxation that we gently let expand to include the mind and then the whole self. A gentle feeling and experiencing of the

---

137 A Better Life, p111

relaxation- the opposite of tension, gripping, contraction, trying or striving.

Physical relaxation is the path to mental relaxation but, the shortest path available is preferable to the long, winding road.

The eyes. Today, unlike when **RWD** was written, many people spend a lot of time focussing closely on the screens of various digital devices etc. The additional cue of letting your eyes focus on the horizon or far distance will help to learn the feeling of relaxing them. You can gently achieve a similar feeling with the lids loosely closed. This is the natural relaxed position of the eyelids and protects the eye surface (the cornea) while you are meditating[138]. In the relaxed position, with lids closed, there is a glimmer of light shining through.

The hands and face. Remember, that the amount of sensation and contraction control in different parts of the body varies and so does the intensity of the letting go sensation. The hands and face are supplied with more nerve connections[139] so you can feel them relax more vividly than some other areas. Meares emphasised feeling the relaxation in the hands and face – especially the forehead and sides of the forehead. **The face and forehead are close to the seat of the mind.** Relaxing these areas helps the relaxation spread to the mind.

Simpler Prompts

"Please do not get the feeling that mental ataraxis [ie. The stillness experience] *is something complicated. It isn't... It is only the words that we have to use to describe it that make it seem complicated.*[140]*"* Stillness Meditation is *"very simple indeed; like the thoughts and feelings of a child, so simple, so difficult, for adults to comprehend."*[141]

Stillness is a mental state without words. A state without thoughts as the mind is resting. A book involves reading words – the vehicle of explanation. Describing the time, place and structure of relaxation is easy. The what do you actually do is harder to explain as it is a "non verbal" process. It is not about words but feeling and experience. The words point to the simple feeling and experiencing of the relaxation, first in the body and then in the mind.

Trains of thought in the RWD period were used to communicate simple ideas to be presented to the mind. Each idea communicates a feeling you then experience (eg feeling your legs relax). A very simple process. But to write or read about this simple process involves a

---

138 The Wealth Within, pp42-43
139 Discussion of motor and sensory nervous system is beyond scope.
140 The Wealth Within p32
141 A Way of Doctoring, p18

sentence. Each sentence, a line from a train of thought, is a reminder or prompt of feeling to experience ie. you gently let yourself experience each one without critical thought. Passive understanding rather than striving comprehension.

Trains of thought, from before 1960 until the 1970s, are set out below. **Don't bother to memorise them** – they are presented to show how they evolved and became simpler prompts.

The first train of thought was to teach "meditating on calmness", while laying on a hard surface, before **1960**:[142]

You are not asleep.
You just let yourself go.
You let yourself go completely.
Feel yourself drift into greater and greater calm.
Feel it all through you,
all through you.
Feel the calm of it in your face.
The muscles of your face are calm.
You feel the calm of it in your mind.
Utter calm.
Complete serenity.
More and more.
All through you.

In **1963**[143], still using the laying down posture the train went as follows:

Good
Muscles of your arms let go.
All your muscles let go.
Legs relaxed, too.
All the muscles of your body let go.
Relaxed, easy, comfortable
Muscles of your stomach let go, too.
Everything lets go. Everything relaxed.
All the muscles of your body relaxed.
It is in your face too.
Feel the muscles of your face relax.
Feel it in the sides of your forehead.
The muscles around your eyes are relaxed.
The muscles of your jaw are loose.
You feel it.
Everything lets go.
Muscles of your face relaxed and calm.

---

142 J Clin Exp Hypnosis 8(4): 237-241. 1960
143 The Management of the Anxious Patient, p272-274

You feel the calm of it.
It is all through you.
You feel the calm of it in your mind.
All through you, relaxed, calm, easy in yourself.
You do it. You do it yourself.
I will sit down over here while you relax.
You do it yourself.
You feel it in your face.
It is all through you.

The **1967 Relief without Drugs (RWD)** trains would be inserted in this chronological sequence here. The next train, Meares wrote for the normal young student anxious about study and exams. Meares noted that **RWD** was more suitable for students having more severe nervous symptoms. So, here is that **1969** train:[144]

I just let myself go.
The weight of my legs on the floor.
I feel the weight of arms resting.
Feel myself sinking into the chair.
So relaxed.
I feel I am drifting.
Feel it in my face.
Jaw muscles are relaxed.
Jaw muscles are so relaxed my lips part and
my jaw sags with its natural weight.
My eyes close as I relax.
The muscles around my eyes,
I feel them relax.
Feel the muscles of my face as I relax.
Feel my forehead smooth out.
Feel the sides of the forehead relax

Our body is relaxed.
We are relaxed.
It is all through us.
Feel this.
Experience it.
It is natural.
You do not have to make yourself relax.
You do not have to do anything.
It is there
You just let it come.
It is quite effortless.

---

144 Student Problems & a Guide to Study, p84, p88

It feels good.
We enjoy it
We experience the feeling of the relaxation of our body;
we experience it in our mind.

Meares began facilitating groups by the late 1960s. Below, are prompts he used in large group sessions prior to **1971**:[145]

Good.
Easy.
Natural.
It's all effortless.
Utterly natural.
Just letting ourselves go.
All effortless.
Natural.
We experience the ease of our body.
It's all through us.
Natural.
Through our whole being.
Deeply.
Just letting ourselves go with it.
Letting go freely.
Ease of it all.
Relaxation of our body.
In our face, in our mind.

Before **1975** another large group session train he reported was[146]:

We are just going to let ourselves relax
very completely.
Let ourselves be at ease while the others come in.
Good.
Easy.
Effortless.
Letting ourselves go.
Ease of it all.
Ease of our body.
Ease of our mind.
Relaxation of our body.
In our face, in our mind.

One compilation[147], citing a 1970s Meares' article, lists the following phrases: *"Good Easy Natural Letting yourself go Effortless All effortless and natural All through us Deeply All through our body*

---

145 Med J Aust 2:675-676. 1971

146 Hypnosis in the Seventies. (Ed) LE Uneståhl. pp110-112. 1975

147Coryndon Hammond, D (1990) Handbook of Hypnotic Suggestions and Metaphors, p160-161. This train is indicative only; primary source unsighted.

All through our mind That's right"

During the **RWD** period the trains appeared in Meares' publications and he uttered them in his group sessions. Sometimes they were written line by line in italics, sometimes as blocks of text with dashes or dots used to represent pauses. By the mid 1970s, in the Stillness Meditation period, his publications contain no trains. Instead, he wrote paragraphs of free flowing text. If you remove the italics and reformat, the train becomes free flowing text. The format is irrelevant! The words are just a vehicle to convey the simple ideas to be experienced.

By the 1980s in his group sessions when Meares spoke it was usually a word or two, here and there, letting silence fill the air for much of the time. One day in mid-1984[148] he ceased using words but continued uttering even simpler calming sounds (*Mmmm* etc) and using calming touch during meditation class.

In 1986[149] Meares wrote down some simple prompts for persons learning to teach Stillness Meditation. They are summarised here without the gaps and pauses that were to be used: *"Good; That's right."... "All resting; Feel the relaxation; Everything relaxed; Face relaxed; Eyes relaxed; Our whole self relaxed; In our face; In our mind; Our mind relaxed; Easy, natural, effortless; More Body relaxed; Mind relaxed; Its all through us; The calm of it; Calm in our mind; More; Good; Really good."* Today, teachers of Meares' method continue to use similar prompts at the start of class for a few minutes, then intermittently, and gradually lapse into silence. Today's teachers use hands placed on the head and shoulders to help communicate calm.

Some people use a few prompts like these simple ones at the start of their own Stillness Meditation practice. An easy gentle slowing prelude to stillness. Other people prefer just feeling the bodily relaxation.

The prompts are like the star pointing finger or a bridge. The **RWD** trains of thought let you wind your way towards, slowly approach and drift across the bridge. **In Stillness Meditation you use the simplest prompts you are able to.** These simpler prompts shorten the bridge so you drift across it closer to the start.

After you cross the bridge, you let go of all prompts as the non-verbal letting go of effortless relaxation quietly supervenes and the journey into the ebb and flow of stillness continues. Stillness lies in the gaps between thoughts and words.

---

148 My personal account. Confirmed by others present around this time.
149 A Better Life, p55, p68. A slightly paraphrased selection.

Let The Relaxation Effortlessly Come

"No one can force himself to relax. It is just an effortless experience.[150]" "We use our will to sit down and practice physical relaxation... Here the use of our will ceases, and we just let the meditation come... We don't strive, we just let go of ourselves. More than this, we just let ourselves...[151]"

"Physical letting go is the pathway to the meditative state[152]"

Tension is trying. Relaxation is the reverse - letting go. Trying or making muscles contract is the opposite of letting go. The mind can't be relaxed precisely like a muscle but it can participate in bodily relaxation with the letting go feeling. A bit like drifting into sleep except you are neither drowsy nor unconscious; you are in a slightly uncomfortable position. You gently fall to stillness rather than sleep.

If there is a problem it is that meditating in this way is too easy! Trying to relax, or trying to do anything is not a part of it. Trying stops the effortlessness. It comes easily and naturally if you just let go. Nothing could be more natural than letting yourself experience this ease which is a part of all humans. No trying. No doing. No striving. No forcing. No making. Rather, an easy, effortless experience.

Unwanted thoughts. When you first start this kind of meditation, it is likely that your mind will return to everyday matters. Some people say "I just can't make my mind go blank". This indicates that they are trying to make it go blank. This is not what is wanted. There is no effort. The whole process is effortless because it is natural to relax in this way. All we have to do is to let it come, quite effortlessly.

If at first you find that your mind returns to everyday topics, don't let it worry you. Even highly placed experienced eastern meditators confided to Meares that unwanted thoughts were sometimes a problem. The solution:[153] *"Unwanted thoughts that are realistic can be quietened simply by feeling the relaxation of our body...[154] we feel the relaxation of our arms... And the same with our legs... And our face. We feel the relaxation of our face muscles..."* Below, is the same idea as a train[155]:

Arms are just flopped.
Feel them relaxed.

---

150 Why Be Old, p50
151 A Better Way, pp116-117
152 McKinnon P, In Stillness Conquer Fear (1994 Ed), p168
153 The Wealth Within, p30
154 Ellipsis reflect editing for brevity rather than the original text
155 Student Problems and a Guide to Study, p86

Face muscles.
How loose.
Muscles around the eyes.
Relaxed.
Feel it deeply.
Whole body.
And its in my mind.
Sinking into the chair with it.

Unrushed. Gently. Quietly. You let yourself experience these simple feelings. In this way going over everyday problems is avoided as you experience the easy, letting go of relaxation. Your mind experiences the relaxation and this yields to a gentle non-verbal letting go.

When you have finished your session, you may realise that your mind has been flitting around various topics that may even seem random. This is similar to normal reverie. It is only mentioned to contrast it as different from going over or worrying about everyday things.

When you have had a little experience of Stillness Meditation, you will notice – afterwards! - that you have not been thinking of anything at all, and that the process was effortless. You will know what Meares meant that thoughts ebb and flow, slow and peter out and, in the gaps, the mind becomes still.

Transcend Minor Discomfort Without Effort

"...we meditate in a posture that is slightly uncomfortable... we let our mind transcend the slight discomfort"[156]

Meares emphasised the importance of meditating in initial minor discomfort ie slight but not overwhelming discomfort. When learning the stillness, **simply sitting in a chair in class and your solo practice is sufficient.** You could use static back (see p112) in your solo practice.

If the posture is slightly uncomfortable the mind relaxes as it transcends the slight discomfort without effort. But, too little or too much discomfort is not what is wanted.

Overwhelming discomfort will result in tensing and trying to endure it. This will interfere with the process of relaxation. Tensing up to endure will harden the mind up with a loss of sensitivity. This is not what is wanted. What is wanted is sensitivity with ease. This is the outcome of effortless mental relaxation transcending slight discomfort.

Too little discomfort – **being too comfortable - will result in drowsiness or sleep** rather than a clear still mind. Do <u>not</u>

---

156 A Better Life, pp106-126

practice lying on a bed or comfy sofa. If you do, the nerves in the limbs and torso will report to the brain that they are relaxed. While feeling pleasant this has little effect in lowering the level of anxiety.

Meares wrote of a sequence of postures to keep a similar slight level of discomfort as your skill slowly improved. It was the slight stimulus, rather than posture as such that was important. The discomfort of posture is not the only potential stimulus in daily life. Other **stimuli** include distraction, disturbance and variety. Meares could not bring these stimuli into the class room. Instead, he wrote about them.

It is important to appreciate that Meares' Stillness Meditation is very simple. Postures and the other stimuli, are not an addition. Rather, they are repeating the simple experience of stillness in slightly challenging situations - making the stillness more general (see later).

Additions Remove Stillness From Meditation [157]

Do not cultivate an awareness of breathing. Deeply relaxed people breathe slowly but focussing on breathing prevents stillness.

Mantras or chanting involves thinking of word(s) and uttering the sounds as these things prevent stillness.

Candle gazing or visualising a pleasant scene in the mind's eye gives the mind something to do. The senses are active in thought and experience of the imagery. In stillness there is no focus or doing.

Spontaneous sensory phenomena sometimes occur in meditation such as coloured lights or feelings of floating etc. They are a distraction from stillness. Sensation is active and this prevents stillness.

All these potential additions give the meditator something to do. It is true that they dull the mind down to fewer thoughts but, there is effort and thought or sensation. These additions remove the stillness. If repeatedly added into meditation the habit becomes an obstacle that must be removed by further practice before the meditator can just let go and create the circumstances where stillness emerges.

Likewise, getting too comfortable feels deceptively pleasant. But this is a physical sensation which does not arise from the mind as such. It is the nerves in the limbs and torso sending signals to the brain. This is distinct from the mental relaxation that occurs when effortlessly transcending minor discomfort from which stillness emerges.

Stillness Meditation simply accesses a natural function: the homeostatic mechanism(s) that permits the mind to become still and experience natural mental rest. In Stillness Meditation, there is

---

157 J Amer Soc Psychsom Dent & Med 25(4)129-132 1978

physical relaxation, we let this relaxation encompass the body, mind, the whole being; thoughts peter out and the mind becomes still. There can be no additions to the meditation to make it better. No mantras or chanting. No focus on breathing. No candle gazing or visualising imagery. No seeking out of sensory phenomena. No getting too comfortable. **Additions subtract stillness from the meditation.**

3.5 Making The Stillness More General

Where do we meditate? Anywhere and everywhere....[158]
"By meditating in different places and at different times, we do not confine the meditation to one particular place... the transcendence of the distraction of meditating outside is the beginnings of the transcendence of the distractions of everyday life"[159]

"Not always practising in the same posture but in different positions... Sometimes outside. And when the student becomes more proficient, meditating in situations in which he has to transcend various distracting influences. All these factors facilitate the on-flow of the effects of our meditation into our daily life."[160]

Meares emphasised that effortless transcendence of minor discomfort was crucial to the flow on of calm. **First, learn the stillness, in just one posture and similar circumstances.** This makes it easier to learn. There is a small amount of postural discomfort to relax through but little extraneous stimuli.

A slightly uncomfortable posture permits the learning of stillness. Such a posture (with no other stimulus) will permit meditation with a flow on, in the class room or in solo practice, that may be experienced as profound. After you have learnt the stillness you experience it with small amounts of additional stimuli present.

You experience the stillness, in slightly challenging situations. These challenges include the slight discomfort of different postures, distraction, disturbance and variety. Effortlessly transcending the slight discomfort of these stimuli helps make the stillness, and the flow on to daily life, more general.

Too little or too much stimuli is not wanted. Overwhelming stimuli will result in tensing and trying to endure. Endurance, with its teeth gritting attitude, is not effortless letting go and stops relaxation.

Over-reaching with too much stimuli may result in the meditator becoming tense. Little steps are important. You make little changes in a series of tiny steps that eventually walk a long distance.

Meares wrote about these things as it was unrealistic to reproduce the stimuli in the class room. So, the experience of stillness in the presence of slightly challenging stimuli lies outside of class.

A Progressive Postural Sequence

In **RWD**, postures were formal, symmetrical and slightly uncomfortable. Use of sitting, lying or squatting was based on

---

158 A Better Life, pp106-126
159 A Better Life, pp120-121; Am J Clin Hyp 25(2-3):114-121. 1983
160 A Better Life, pp66-67

individual needs. There was also advice to add further slight discomfort eg lay on pebbles, sit with a small clip on an arm etc.

After RWD (ie by mid-1970s), *"By changing about the circumstances of our meditation we develop the idea that the ease of our mind is with us whatever we are doing.[161]"* and *"We must keep changing our posture as we become progressively more experienced in our meditation[162]"* Meares[163] wrote a sequence of postures but, **everyone was to use one easy posture to learn the stillness.**

After having learnt the stillness in that first posture (eg sitting), people were to move along Meares' sequence in a series of small steps. They were to use the slightly challenging stimulus provided by a second posture many times. Then they were to introduce the third only when the second was easy. And so on. Over time meditating in one and then another posture the level of initial discomfort in the final posture would be more than the former. But, it was always set at a minor level that could be effortlessly transcended by the meditator.

Posture is always matched to individual ability. A healthy younger person is likely to progress faster and further along the progression than an immobile, sick or elderly person. The latter must, as needs have it, progress at a slower sensible rate. The level of initial slight discomfort needs to be appropriate **for each individual**.

A posture should never cause pain. Firstly, too much stimulus results in the teeth grinding attitude of endurance which also prevents stillness. Secondly, and more importantly, remember Meares warning regarding pain: in this case this means avoiding any overtly painful meditation posture until you know the cause.

After you know the cause then possible solutions might include avoiding certain postures, using one that shifts weight (or gravity) off or away from the sore area, stretches it less or is a step back to an easier posture that is merely slightly uncomfortable. For some people, meditating while sitting on a chair may be the best option[164].

Seniors and some sick people may only be able to sit. Meares wrote that slight discomfort from sitting on a hard seat with torso unsupported was a suitable goal for some sick or elderly people.[165] People just sitting receive the mental rest of stillness.[166] The main purposes of meditation posture are to prevent sleep and provide the same initial level of discomfort to be transcended by the mind. If that is met using a seat then it (the seat) is a sufficient challenge for

---

161 172 The Wealth Within, p35

162 A Better Life. p117

163 The Wealth Within, pp33-47

164 The Wealth Within, p53

165 The Wealth Within, p53

166 McKinnon P, Living Calm in a Busy World, p103

that individual. Sitting, without progression, with torso unsupported may be all that is eventually suitable for some unwell or elderly people[167] and is sufficient.[168] Such people may use different chairs when meditating in different places. Later on, they may turn to other stimuli to add a slight progressive challenge.

Movement ability and "harder" postures. If you are able, then **slowly and sensibly** working up to the more challenging postures may improve movement ability (eg flexibility, range of movement). Along similar lines, if it is sensible to attempt it, being able to safely sit on the floor and get up unaided also offers physical health benefits.[169]

Stillness Meditation helps integrate nerve impulses and thus reduces anxiety. Ill health, from organic disease, can generate additional nerve impulses that the brain must integrate.[170] In some cases, improved alignment and movement ability may reduce nerve impulses resulting from the disease (eg joint disease).

"Harder" postures deepen the stillness as the mind effortlessly transcends a comparatively larger stimulus.[171] [172]

As you proceed, in tiny steps, along the postural sequence the mind is relaxed. More muscles hold the posture. They are also working more to hold a less supported position. Some are being gently stretched. Meares also emphasised a stable, upright posture eg cross-legged sitting up straight and tall. These things together pose a larger challenge which the mind learns to relax though.

Meares' Sequence. First are the **sitting postures**, Meares noted that a stiff neck could result if the head flopped forwards[173]. Assume an upright balanced posture and remember there needs to be some minimal muscle tone to hold the torso and neck upright. Meares also mentions that an arm placed palm down over a hard or edged arm rest could compress the radial nerve.[174] The use of chairs with a soft arm (or no arm) will help prevent the arm pressing against another surface if it were to shift during meditation. Alternatively, hands can be placed palm up or down on each leg or in the lap. These measures should help to minimise any risk of compression.

Sitting - using an arm chair
Sitting - using a straight backed chair without arm rests

---

167 The Wealth Within, p53
168 McKinnon P, Living Calm in a Busy World, p103
169 Brito, Ricardo, Araújo et al. (2014) Euro J Prev Cardiol 21(7):892-8
170 Life without Stress, pp27-31
171The Wealth Within, p48
172 Gawler, I Peace of Mind, p48, p78
173 The Wealth Within, pp42-43
174 The Wealth Within, pp42-43

Sitting - using straight back chair or stool in "Pharaoh position" In the Pharaoh position you sit with your back away from the chair so it is unsupported. You sit tall with your forearms on your thighs. Crossing the legs at the ankles later on is a step towards sitting cross legged. The next step being to use a slightly lower chair or stool.

The lying postures require that you are able to get down onto the floor - and back up again later (with help, if required). Lying is useful for people having difficulty learning to relax as gravity helps the limbs and torso settle back into the floor.

Lying static back.[175] The calves are placed onto a seat or stool with knees bent to about 90 degrees. Arms are flat out on the floor away from the torso with palms up.

Always use the floor. Start with a pillow or book under your head if needed. Lower the height little by little. Gravity helps the relaxation. Static back is quite different from the position people usually sleep in. It is used as a "rest position" for various conditions and helps postural alignment provided by the sinking that gravity facilitates as it shifts several joints towards the one plane.

Lying on floor arms by sides. Meares mentions adjustments for inflexible people but it is easier to use static back.

The first step towards **kneeling** is to reduce the height you sit with crossed legs (eg lower chair or stool) in a series of steps.

Kneeling - knees bent and hips straight. Knees slightly wider than hips. Hands may be placed hanging at the side of the body.

Kneeling - with cushion between the haunches and the ankles. Or the feet could be placed under a low stool ("seiza" style) on which you sit. The hands may be placed on the thighs.

Cross-legged on floor - sit on a cushion. Arms can hang loosely at the sides or rest in the lap. The whole of the head, neck, and back is unsupported. A solid stable stool or solid stable stack of books can be used. Later you might use a cushion. After time has been spent reducing the height in series of steps you sit on the floor. If sitting cross legged with your torso unsupported is difficult you could try initially cross legged with the upper body against a wall.

Cross-legged on floor - one foot (eg left) on top of the opposite (right) knee and the left shin resting on the right lower leg. It is a good idea to alternate which leg is on top to avoid asymmetry which might eventually adversely influence posture.

When sitting cross-legged, men should place the heels apart and away from the mid-line (and a little further forward if necessary). This will avoid the heel(s) squeezing the delicate urinary tube (ureter)

---

175 Egoscue P, The Egoscue Method of Health Through Motion. 1992

against the underside of the hip bones.[176]

It should be mentioned that some sick or old people may find that they only move a couple of steps along the sequence. They may be able to use these steps to meditate in postures that cover many of the positions assumed in daily life ie bent and straight legs and torso oriented at right angles and parallel to gravity. For example, sitting, static back and lying on the floor.

Adding new postures. Meares believed that additions to his method might result in a loss rather than a gain. A "new" posture would need to be formal, symmetrical and slightly uncomfortable with valid reasons for use including safer progression or as a modification to avoid accumulating or aggravation of injury or disease. Static back, unknown in Meares time, is one example.

Same Posture, Different Discomfort

There are several ways to vary discomfort in the same posture:

Sensible stretching by changing the position slightly to effect a gentle stretch eg pulling crossed legs closer in as do yogis etc. Stretching may not always be an option for a particular posture.

Alter the surface on which you are positioned eg. smooth to rougher or tepid to cooler (carpet to wood to tiled to stone floor). For example, using a different chair with a hard seat pan.

Add an object to the surface which increases pressure at the point of placement underneath the meditator such as placing rounded pebbles, books or other carefully chosen harmless objects.

Change the chair or furniture used[177] such as a differently shaped seat pan, back and or arms, missing arms or back and or different fabric covering and so on. Remember Meares' caution regarding placing an arm over an arm rest (especially if hard or edged) as this could press on the radial nerve[178]. One solution is to place the upper limb away from the arm rest so that it is unlikely to slip and contact the rest during Stillness Meditation. Furniture includes "ergonomic" chairs that involve different positions to ordinary chairs eg the Balam chair[179], the saddle chair etc although some people may find the Balam chair etc awkward to get on\off. People using exercise balls as a seat have slipped or fallen off when sitting doing things; the risk of a slip or fall would be increased during Stillness Meditation and so exercise balls cannot be recommended.

People who have moved along Meares' postural progression may also find they use the seats available where kneeling and so on would

---

176 The Wealth Within, pp42-43
177 Really a combination of altering the surface,object, stretching
178 The Wealth Within, pp42-43
179 Gawler, I Peace of Mind.

soil work clothing or would best be avoided.

Clips (eg paper or surgical clips) may be placed on folds of skin (eg on forearm) to create a slightly uncomfortable pinching pressure that could be transcended without effort.

Distractions And Environmental Variety

In life, we are surrounded by unwanted sound, environmental variation and distraction. So, after the experience gained in secure surroundings it is useful to practice without shutting out the sounds of the city and of nature. Practice in various surroundings such as the garden, the park, the athletics track, near the pool or at the beach. Practice outside in the cold or heat, at dawn or dusk, at night or in the light of day and, in weather of all sorts.

Clothed And Fewer Clothes

Sometimes, it may be useful to practice in as few clothes as possible without offending others or even naked (ie. in privacy eg the bathroom). Meares believed that this enhanced the naturalness of Stillness Meditation, a sense of unity and the true simplicity of life.

In cooler weather less (or minimal) clothing can contribute to relaxing through the distraction of cold discomfort. Meares himself, meditated in uncomfortable cold situations eg outside in Melbourne winter.

Some "hard" eastern practitioners take cold situations as far as ice and snow and immersing themselves in icy cold water. Such situations carry risks that substantially outweigh the benefits. Frostbite and or hypothermia can cause permanent injury that can be life altering or, if severe, fatal. For these and other reasons such practices are to be avoided.

Different Times Of Day

At the start, pick times that permit regular daily practice to help get into the habitual pattern of 20-45 mins split over 2-3 sessions a day.

The first session could be shortly after you get up. Outside at dawn, after the shower, before or after breakfast, on public transport or after arriving at work. The second (and third) sessions could be at lunch time, during a work break, after work is finished, on public transport or after arriving home. It might be before physical exercise or after exercise as part of recovery. Or choose other workable times each day that help get into the habit of daily practice.

Next, after you have established the regular pattern, when changes in your schedule create extra time, then some of it might be used to meditate. This could be the next session brought forward, freeing up time for other things later in the day.

The starting times of sessions can also be varied a little. For example, a session in the morning say at some point between getting up and before leaving home. Retain the habit of regular practice but vary the time.

Meditating at different times will help make the stillness more general and not limited to the times of practice. Cultivation of the calm in daily life will also help make the flow on independent of time.

Safe Stimuli Of Sudden Onset

Meares wrote that in making use of the ideas described you will gain experience and become somewhat used to discomfort, distraction and variety. Later on, practise should advance to situations where the meditator was subject to sudden, unpredictable stimuli. This establishes a pattern for coping with sudden frustration. Start with something easy, for example, meditating outside in gusts of wind that creates sensations on your skin and tousles your hair. These are fairly easy stimuli to be calmly disregarded. Perhaps next, you might advance to learning to calmly disregard the slightly stronger stimulus of sitting near a tree with drooping branches (eg weeping willow) so that gusts of wind bring the branches to sweep into contact with you. If there is no suitable tree available, then perhaps a curtain (or sheet) might be hung on a clothes line with the meditator positioned adjacent to it. If you have friendly pets perhaps you can meditate where the dog\ cat will sit on your feet, lick hands or jump onto your lap. These are all examples of letting go of disturbance.

In summer, Meares meditated near a rotating sprinkler that showered him. He also used sea spray generated by waves crashing onto rocks at the beach to similar effect. If neither of these are available then perhaps, a slowly dripping shower rose or hose that splashes drops onto the skin every few minutes might be contrived. Harmless insects buzzing around the face on a summers day could serve a similar purpose.

In the modern electronic world there are other opportunities to create random or intermittent stimuli. Some fans will change direction and fan speed to a variable extent and so create intermittent gusts of wind. Timers might be set to create a disturbing audible (but not deafening) noise at intervals.

Remember to match the difficulty of these stimuli to your ability to relax through them. They should be slightly disturbing (ie slightly uncomfortable) but not overwhelmingly so. If you find that you start to respond just after the stimulus has occurred you simply relax a little more, regain you composure and continue to let yourself go into Stillness Meditation. If you find that you are tensing up after each

---

stimulus then the challenge is too great and needs to be reduced to enable further gentle easy effortless practice to occur. After that you will soon find that you will barely notice the stimulus. For example, there is a noise. You barely hear a sound and it has no meaning. Your mind disregards the sound. You may not even recall it afterwards. If the noise is too loud for your level of slight challenge and you find yourself responding to it you regain your composure. You do this by letting yourself relax deeper into the stillness. In this regard, it may be useful to know that sound without information (eg truck backfiring) is easier to work with than the sounds of speech. As your ability to work with these stimuli improves you will find that they, the stimuli, will deepen the stillness.

Meares used black and white examples to help educate the reader in understanding the principles of stimuli of sudden onset. He peripherally mentions the pinnacle of sudden onset stimuli, the martial methods of "hard" Zen schools, where the meditator might be struck by an assistant using a cane or similar. In a medieval battle, being wounded without impairment of relentless counter attack was desirable and might be a down payment on survival. In modern times, martial practices need a martial framework and even then may inadvertently cross the line between safety and injury. Meares' meditation is modern. It has a health based rather than a martial orientation. But, Meares' martial example highlights the usefulness of an ability to remain calm, or go even deeper into calm, in unusual or emergency situations. Perhaps, this is how nature intended humans should respond to dire situations. To respond to the hand of cards dealt to us by fate by living calm, and with ease, selecting and executing the best effective action available in the circumstances. If this is true, civilisation has resulted in many of us becoming separated from a valuable part of our heritage.

Unusual Interruptions To Daily Routine

Interruptions to your routine may sometimes occur. But, you can think through what you might do, in terms of options, to help to ensure that some Stillness Meditation occurs that day.

All you need is a place where you will not be disturbed for 10-20 minutes. Explanation to others, signs, closed doors and even locked ones may be helpful. You may be able to choose a position where people will just know to leave you be. Cars, cubicles, empty meeting rooms and other unexpected places might be able to be used.

A session may be shortened rather than missed. Another session may be lengthened. An extra session can be added to catch up for one unavoidably missed. Also, remember the opurtunities posed by extra time when appointments or activities are cancelled or varied. You could proactively "interrupt" your routine with a Stillness Meditation session!

Rarely will none of these options be possible. If none are possible, then it is best to ensure that the interrupted day remains an unusual exception. Missing a Stillness Meditation session or daily practice for a day is one thing but, if continued, would begin to undermine the regular habit you are cultivating as well as time in which natural mental rest was absent denying the mind relaxation and restoration.

3.6 Living Calm [180 181 182]

Meares emphasised the importance of the flow on of effortless calm during normal consciousness and daily life. Or *"learning the calm, experiencing the calm and, ultimately, living the calm".*[183]

If nothing is done but Stillness Meditation the calm will flow into daily life anyway, of its own accord. But, certain practices help encourage the seepage of the flow of calm from stillness into daily life.

Look Forward To And Like Your Practice

Meares emphasised that those people who come to like meditating do best. So, gently and easily bring yourself to look forward to Stillness Meditation. Bring yourself to enjoy it and the feeling of calm and ease that flows on afterwards. This is not hard to do! Soon it becomes something you look forward to. You will soon find that you come to like the experience of Stillness Meditation itself.

Capture The Feeling As You Finish

Meares advised sitting for a couple of minutes after you have just finished meditating and experience the feeling of the flow on of calm and ease. This is to encourage it and also help be able to recall the feeling during daily life.

If you feel a little glassy eyed or drowsy after meditation then a few minutes rest is a good idea anyway. A little time to re-balance will allow reorientation back into the practical realities of everyday life.

In the mid-1980s, at the end of group sessions, Meares said[184]:

mmmmmmMMM

Good.

That was good.

Just let your eyes open now

Just let ourselves rest quietly for a moment.

As you finish your own session remind yourself in a similar way. You quietly sit. You let your eyes open, rest and feel the calm and ease through you. How it feels in the face, hands and body. So you can remember the feeling later on as you go about doing things.

Cultivate The Calm In Daily Life

During Stillness Meditation, you experience natural mental rest.

---

180 J Helen Vale Found 2(4):10-14. 1980

181 Am J Clin Hypnosis 25(2-3):114-121. 1983

182 Yoga Quarterly 14(4):27-32. 1979

183 McKinnon P, Living Calm in a Busy World, p84

184 A Better Life, p60

You become aware of the calm and ease of mind at the end of the session. You feel the ease all through you so you can remember it and recall this later. Next, you bring this feeling into your ordinary life. You just effortlessly recall the feeling and the effortless calm is there in your mind. At first, you do this by recalling the experience of it. You feel the relaxation of your mind. You are conscious of the ease and are aware of the relaxation of the face muscles and the calm of mind.

The very easiest time is at the end of Stillness Meditation. Next is when you are sitting, standing or have assumed some other stationary position at another time. If you do exercises with static postures (eg an exercise where a single position is held like "the plank") the lack of movement makes it comparatively easy to recall the feeling of ease. Just remember this is not meditation as such, but you aim to experience the feeling of ease with a clear mind.

Next is moving. It is easiest to pick simple repetitive tasks that you can do fairly easily. For example, slow moving (physically) flowing exercises lend themselves well to feeling the onwards flow. Walking, gentle calisthenics (repetitive exercises), light aerobic activity or joint mobility are examples. Slightly more variable tasks are doing routine household tasks. Or simple rhythmical activities that require a little more work like skipping or jogging.

Meares said that increasingly over time you will find that some of the effortless calm stays there of its own accord, and you will be aware that your mind has found a smoother, easier way of functioning.

Cat-Naps Before Unusual Situations

"Little cat-naps of meditation can be a help just before some potentially stressful situation such as an important interview or exam"[185]

There is only this one mention of cat-naps in his last book. Meares suggested that a short Stillness Meditation cat-nap just before certain difficult situations (eg exams, job interviews) would generate flow onwards that would then be present to help cope. The use of a cat-nap was infrequent and unusual and not for day to day situations.

The cat-nap is a step across the threshold into meditation rather than just recalling the sense of calm and ease at another time of day; the method Meares recommended for the vast majority of the time.

Rest If Sleep Eludes

Generally speaking, people who have learnt to meditate sleep well. However, Stillness Meditation may not cure a traumatic injury, noisy neighbours, an ill spouse or similar circumstances that might

---

185 A Better Life, p67

curtail sleep. Meares advised: *"lie flat on your back in bed. You let the tranquillity come to your mind which you learned lying on the floor. When you have got it properly, you let tranquillity mingle with drowsiness. Then...roll over into your usual position of sleep. And that's it. You are asleep"*[186]

To learn this useful skill Meares advised:*"commence your meditation in some posture of slight discomfort... If you are concerned about sleep it is best to do it lying flat on your back on the floor."* [187] Slight discomfort means the relaxation comes from the mind. The slight discomfort also helps prevent sleep at the time you are learning the mental relaxation. Only use a bed, sofa or similar comfort when you wish to sleep. If sleep eludes then use Meares' method to get some rest.

Read Some Of Meares' Poems [188]

In Zen, the koan is accorded very high status. The student of Zen spends hours a day pondering a single koan. Some schools of Zen emphasise the koan ahead of meditation! Of course, in the Meares method it is meditation first. But, if you have not read some of Meares' therapeutic poetry then you may be missing out.

Meares wrote that: "[some of his] *poetry books be left lying about, be picked up and a few pages read here and there in the idle moment"*. [Patients found his poetry] *"added very greatly to their understanding of meditative experience"*. [It]*"facilitates the onflow of the non-verbal philosophical understanding of meditation."*

Several poems have been published in various books, magazines and online etc. These previously disclosed poems have preferentially been utilised as samples in the following pages rather than quoting them at the start of each chapter\section and at various points within the text. This will enable the reader to sample, a couple at a time, as Meares intended. It is a preview of the 900 or so poems contained in his books that can be found in some libraries or sourced second hand from bookshops or the internet. Dip into the samples, taste the flavours and source the book(s) you think might resonate.

Meares himself recommended **From the Quiet Place** and **Dialogue on Meditation** to his readers and patients[189]. These together with **A Kind of Believing** were also published as a trilogy entitled **Dialogue on Meditation --From the Quiet Place - A Kind of Believing. Section** 1.5 has a list of the poetry books and also indicates the number of poems in each book.

---

186 Life without Stress pp79-81; Also S2.4.1 Particular Symptoms
187 Life without Stress pp79-81
188 Am J Clin Hypnosis 25(2-3):114-121. 1983.
189 A Better Life p17

4. Samples Of Poems By Ainslie Meares

A Glimpse in Idle Moments

Preface

To strive,
Create, give birth,
What can an old man do?
Give birth to thought.

To express the inexpressible,
And share with you a glimpse,
Of something far beyond:
Nor heart nor mind.
But the very soul itself.

From *My Soul and I*, p7

We let ourself.
We let ourself go with it,
Body and mind.
We let ourself feel it,
The calm and the ease.
We let it all through us,
The whole of our being.
Just let ourself.
Then we are part of it all.

Let us grow.
A man grows in wisdom,
A woman in understanding,
A boy in strength,
And a girl grows into the future.
How do we grow in ourselves?
We grow in the stillness,
As the child grows in his cot.
It is the stillness of ourself.
And it is in this that we grow

*Both from the book **From the Quiet Place** pp 29&57*

Why keep talking of stillness,
When life is a matter of doing?

Go back.
Go back to where we went wrong.
This is the purpose of stillness.

Go back.
Then forward again on the new path.
Forward.
To what we could not reach before.

Go back.
More than thought and in feeling,
In being.
And new patterns of being arise.

Our body goes back in its being.
Faulty reactions are gone.
New ones arise in their place.
Healing can come,
When none could before.

This is the purpose of stillness.

*From the book **From The Quiet Place**, p47*

It's all in the depth,
In the depth there's the healing.

Where is the depth,
In the heart or the mind?

The depth is above and below,
It is all around,
Way out beyond,
And we are part of it all.

It helps you remember.
A childish game,
A string around the finger.

So much
That's good to remember.

*Both from **CANCER: ANOTHER WAY?** pp 59, 110*

Doctors are human beings
Trained and conditioned
In the science and art of medicine
As it is understood at the time.

Once trained and conditioned,
It is hard to change.
We ourselves know this
From our experience of life.

It is easy to advance new methods
Within the framework of the old.

A new operation for cancer,
And the surgeon will try it.
New drugs are tried,
Even before they're fully tested.
But with something different
It is so very much harder
To break with tradition
And give it a trial.

*From **CANCER: ANOTHER WAY?** p118*

You invite me
to go into meditation,
To a strange country
where I have not been before.

Without a journey
into something new
You stay where you are
Like so many others.

If I were to come to you
What could you give me?

Nothing.
I give nothing at all.
Meditation
Is simply a way
Of releasing
What is already there.

*Both from **Dialogue on Meditation**, pp 2&7*

One thing only
The fullness of love,
Not just love itself
Of which I have some share,
But the fullness.

The fullness of the glass
Is in the stillness of the hand,
The fullness of the bloom
Is in the stillness of the day,
The fullness of love
Is in the stillness within,
The fullness of life
Is in the calm of it all
Where is the calm of it all?
That's what we teach.

*From **Dialogue on Meditation**, p91*

The only knowledge
Is that form of knowing
Which lets us understand
We need not know.

Understanding comes to us,
But we must open the door
Before he can come in.

Enlightenment
by its lack of substances
Slips through the fingers
Just as thistledown
Pursued by a child
On a summer's day.

*Both from **A Kind of Believing**, pp 50&6*

Simple
As the questions of a child,
And so hard to answer.

Simple
As the talk of lovers,
And the meaning so deep.

Let me be simple.
If I know the apple falls,
What need I know of gravity?

There's an essence
Of something simple
In all that's great.

From *A Kind of Believing*, p51

Understanding
Comes as a guiding star
that in a clouded world
Suddenly reveals itself.

Fire burns,
If it does not burn
There is no fire.

Wind blows,
If it does not blow
There is no wind.

I grow,
If I do not grow
I am no longer me.

*Both from **Thoughts**, p21*

Let me look upon your face
For there I see that which is human
And so much more.
Let me share the calm of your spirit
In those moments
When you glimpse the meaning of it all.
Let me share the rapture
Of the fire within,
And in your absence
Let me share
The presence of your being.

*From **Thoughts**, p37*

Long have I known the stillness
Of meditation,
But now there comes
A greater stillness
That does not seem to be
Of mine own self.

Silent,
As in the autumn
When a falling leaf
Reverberates
The dry leaves on which it falls

The wave rolls on
To its death on the beach
And spills the whiteness
We never knew was there.

Beauty is seen and heard
And sometimes
Tasted, smelled or felt,
But there comes another beauty
Which transcends the senses.

Both from **Prayer and Beyond**, *pp4&53*

I leave the clamour of the weary day
And fall into prayer,
And in the stillness of a mountain mist
That part of me
Which is my soul
Unites with something greater.

We let some part of us.
Go out and merge
With that which is greater than ourself;
A stillness -
The nothingness
Brimful of meaning.

And out being
Fills with the essence
Of that which is all about us.

*From **Prayer and Beyond**, p59*

One is weak
And has little understanding,
the other stronger
And perhaps
Understands a little better.
The stronger gives to the weaker,
But he does not give his strength
Or his understanding,
He merely gives something
That reawakens
The strength and understanding
Of the other.

What do we say?
We say very little.
Well, what do we do?
We do very little.
But some miraculous power
Brings a way of doctoring
To mean a very great deal.

*Both from **A Way of Doctoring**, No.14 (p8) & No.21(p11)*

Any event concerning our self
Effects us in different ways,
In material ways
And also at different levels of our being.

In a way of doctoring
By meditation
We let run our mind
In very simple fashion,
Simple like a child,
Simple
Like lower forms of life.

Let us remember
In lower forms of life,
Reptiles, crustaceans, shell fish
The healing power of the body
Is much greater than ours.

In this way of meditation
The cells of our body
Go back to function in the simple way
Of bygone days
Of better healing.

From *A Way of Doctoring*, No41 (p19-20)

The brightest star
Twinkling in the night
Melts into nothingness
At early dawn.

Too bright a light
Blinds the eye.

Let close the eyes,
And we shall see
More clearly
In meditation.

Ease is born and ease begets
Who are the offspring of ease?
The children of ease
Are wisdom and health.

*Both from **LETS BE AT EASE**, pp 49&31*

Ease is quietness of mind
Amid the turmoil of life.

Ease does what has to be done
Without inner unrest.

Ease is at one
With all around us.

Ease conducts our life
In the simple laws of nature.

Ease is a manifestation
Of the smooth working of our mind.

Ease is that state of being
In which we have access to our soul.

*From **LETS BE AT EASE**, p25*

We are part of the world where we live,
More closely a part
Of all that we hold dear.
The tabby cat, our brown eyed spaniel,
The knurled old tree where the magpie nests,
Our nick-nacks on the mantle shelf,
Are so dear to us.
Mother, father, brother, sister.
Our health, our life.
But comes the one,
And the dearness of all else
Fades into oblivion.

The winter sun on leafless trees
Makes patterns on the grass.

Gentle wavelets
Write their message on the sand
Knowing tomorrow it is gone.

But long lasts the message
Of the given rose
Though it fades so soon.

*Both from **MAN AND WOMAN**, No.40(p24) & No.102(p60)*

I trust you in the simple things of life,
My daily earnings and worldly goods.
I trust what you say,
As I know, with you
The spark of truth burns bright.
I trust you freely with those who flaunt
All that the flesh desires.
I trust you with confessions
Of mine own weakness,
For I know that these will never be betrayed.
I trust you with the tender places of my body
For I know no hurt will come
I trust you with my dreams,
My fantasies and hopes,
Those things which to another
Would seem so foolish.
I trust you with those strivings of the spirit
In search of God and understanding.
Which emerge only in the trust of another.

From **MAN AND WOMAN**, *No.100(p59)*

I know
There are intimations
All about me
That can give
Direction to my being.

The lessons of simple things,
The season that is upon us,
The ebb and flow of the tide,
The wind blown leaf,
All go unheeded.

And beyond those outward things
There lies the inner promptings
Of mute silences
That call aloud
The message of the spirit.

From ***The Silver Years***, *p65*
A book of practical advice for a rewarding later life
that also contains 32 poems.

We are older now.
Have been through it all before,
And there comes a reluctance
To attend the party.

The changing pattern of the clouds
Lets in the sun
When we least expect it.

A new light.
Shines on old celebrations.
New meaning comes to us
Which we did not have before.

As time passes
Thought grows deeper,
As the roots
Of the aging tree.

From ***The Silver Years,*** *p218*
A book of practical advice for a rewarding later life
that also contains 32 poems.

Epilogue

And what of this other thing
that comes in the eye of the storm
and in the stillness of night,
 yet resides in a drop of dew?
Cherish it, for it is born of the spirit
and transcends all else.

Last verse of the Epilogue from **THE WEALTH WITHIN**
The only poem in that book and worth a look.

5. Meares' Teaching Protocol and Personal Practises [190]

Meares' Teaching Protocol

People wanting to see Meares contacted his reception to arrange a time to see him.

Meares subsequently met with them, discussion occurred and he provided information about his method. Typically, this was followed by a short private meditation session. People then booked into the meditation classes Meares ran.

They returned to attend meditation class and as each participant arrived Meares met them and ushered them to a seat. When all were seated Meares commenced by uttering a couple of words here and there for a few minutes and then lapsed into silence.

He moved around the room from person to person, using his calming presence and therapeutic touch. Typically placing his hands on the shoulders-upper chest area and then the head, to communicate comfort and reassurance and to facilitate a deepening relaxation.

The class proceeded in this way for about 40 minutes or so. The class finished when Meares uttered a few words to gently rouse the participants. The participants remained seated, rested for a couple of minutes and waited. One by one, Meares accompanied each participant to an adjacent room. He then sought and provided feedback and answered questions.

SMT® and Stillness Meditation teachers still follow a similar protocol.

Meares' Meditation Practise

Over the course of his career Meares was both a guinea pig and walking behavioural model. He tested everything upon himself before he applied each new refinement to the benefit of his patients. He was already practising himself what he recommended others should do. This began with teaching himself how to become calm so that he might be a calming influence upon his patients. It led him to meditate on calm by the late 1950s. The experience of Kathmandu reinforced his belief in meditation, deepened his own sense of calm, but also

---

190 Am J Clin Hypnosis 25(2-3):114-121 1983; The Wealth Within; A Better Life; Confirmed in miscellaneous sources and personal communications.

emphasised the communication of calm from one person to another. His research led him to have teeth extracted without anaesthetic as a living example of pain without hurt. By the mid 1970s he had experimented in this way for removal of 4 teeth and a sebaceous cyst.

By the late 1970s, his own meditation consisted of 15 minutes every morning during the working week as well as the group sessions he facilitated on week days. He fully participated in these sessions and drifted in and out of the meditative state. In this way, Meares meditated for about 45 mins or so each weekday. On weekends, he practised for around an hour each day.

He used a range of postures, discomfort, distraction, variation and sudden stimuli in his own meditation as well as encouraging the flow of calm and ease into daily life.

He wrote koan poetry for his patients: writing it requiring far greater understanding than just reading it (as did his patients).

Other Health Practises

Meares trained as an agricultural scientist and then a medical practitioner became a psychiatrist and earned his doctorate by research on hypnosis. In the area of meditation he was at the leading edge. He was truly a doctor ahead of his time. In other respects his personal health practices tended to be conventional.

Diet. His diet was conventional for the day. In one interview he said his method did not require a special diet as long as basic principles of nutrition were followed and a sound diet consumed.

Sleep is discussed in his writings but he does not mention how much he slept or how much he recommended. He emphasised the natural rest of Stillness Meditation and a method of getting rest when sleep eludes (refer S3).

Physical Activity. He played tennis twice a week. Each day after his morning meditation he went for a leisurely walk in what he described as a beautiful park adjacent to his rooms. The footage[191] of him walking with his cane in the park, in a fluid manner shows that he was in a deep state of relaxation (presumably) cultivating the feeling in his own daily life.

Meares also had farming and country connections and is believed to have spent time in those surroundings and engaged in related activities. These probably included horse riding, walking and working with animals.

---

191 Healers, Quacks or Mystics, Ep.4. Nevill Drury. 1983

6. Learn, Experience & Live Calm

Reading a book plants the seed but, it is learning, experiencing and living the effects of Stillness Meditation that really count.

Learn and Experience the Calm

Stillness Meditation

1. Work out **2-3 suitable times** each day, **a place**, a **seat** to sit on or for lying static back. You may use a (quiet) **timer**.
2. **Times (or points) should each allow 15 mins practice.** Pick points that fit your routine & will nearly always work. Make regular daily practice a habit and have a back up plan to use if your routine is unusually interrupted.
3. **Pick place(s) where you will not be disturbed** for 15 mins. Explanation to others, signs, closed doors and even locked ones may be helpful. You may be able to choose a position where people will just know to leave you be. Cars, cubicles, empty meeting rooms etc might be able to be used. Others could be encouraged to keep (relatively) quiet or engage in tasks a distance away or you might be able to use another location. If noisy activities occur at certain times then avoid them. As a last resort, ear plugs might be used (and abandoned as soon possible). Set digital devices off etc.
4. **Look forward to and like your practice**
5. Sit on your seat, set your timer and begin.
6. **Use the simplest prompts you can.** Meares[192] wrote:*"our mind itself can reduce anxiety.. in a very simple form of.. meditative experience based on 3 principles:"*

1) "Complete physical relaxation in a global fashion."
2) "Experiencing the relaxation so that it pervades our whole being."
3) "Practising in circumstances of slight discomfort which eases as the meditative experience develops"

The simplest prompt is to effortlessly feel a non-verbal letting go that leads into a flow or wave of relaxation.

In Stillness Meditation class the teacher utters prompts in a prelude to the quietness that follows. In your solo practice, you could use a CD[193]. You stop using it when you have the knack. If don't have a CD you may use a few prompts like these: *"Good.. All resting.. Feel the relaxation.. Everything relaxed.. Face relaxed.. Eyes relaxed..*

---

192 Aust Fam Physician 5(7):906-910, 1976. Several quotes from article.
193 McKinnon, P Experiencing Stillness Meditation. CD

Our whole self relaxed.. In our face.. In our mind.. Our mind relaxed.. Easy, natural, effortless.. Body relaxed.. Mind relaxed.. Its all through us.. The calm of it.. Calm in our mind.. More.. Good.. Really good.[194]" After a few minutes you lapse into silence and continue to let go and drift.

If unwanted thoughts arise they *"can be stilled by feeling in our mind our ease of body".[195]* You gently feel relaxation in the hands, face etc in no particular order (or using a toes to top sequence if that is easier). If needed, spend more time letting go of any areas that tend to grip (or re-grip). Keep gently letting go. The relaxation spreads. You continue letting go and drift into stillness.

7. *[Your timer goes off]* **Capture the feeling as you finish** and don't forget to rest for a couple of minutes. If you still feel drowsy or glassy eyed some extra rest will help you re-balance before moving on.

Making The Stillness More General

At the beginning, meditate using just one posture in similar circumstances. This will help make it easier. But, is not forever. Later, after you have learnt the stillness you gradually introduce easy tiny challenges (stimuli), one at a time as outlined in the book. Each little challenge is effortlessly transcended. Do not change too much or too quickly. Tiny steps add up over time to walk a long distance.

Living Calm

Cultivate The Calm Feeling In Daily Life

Plan A Cat-Nap Just Before Unusual Situations

If Sleep Eludes Then Use Meares' Method To Get Some Rest.

Read Some Of Meares' Poems In Idle Moments

---

194 A Better Life, p55, p68. A slightly paraphrased selection.
195 Aust Fam Physician 5(7):906-910, 1976. Several quotes from article.

Other Books

Be aware that some others use "Stillness" to refer to meditation that has absolutely nothing in common with Meares' method. If you look at books not listed below you should check that they are purely about Meares' method or risk either confusion or disappointment.

Of other books solely about the pure Meares method, the easiest to source are by Pauline McKinnon. **Living Calm in a Busy World** gives an excellent view of Meares method based on decades of experience teaching it. **In Stillness Conquer Fear** describes her recovery from agoraphobia- with its apprehensive fear of anxiety- arguably the most unpleasant phobia of them all.

Ray Reardon another teacher who learnt directly from Meares also wrote a book[196] of poetic reflections and images (though hard to locate today).

You already have the essence of **RWD**. Meares also refers the reader to **The Wealth Within, Dialogue on Meditation** and **From the Quiet Place** (the latter two books together with **A Kind of Believing** were published as a trilogy after Meares' death).

For a broader view of Meares' philosophy there is **Lets Be Human. Life Without Stress** and **A Way of Doctoring** are also good if you can track them down. His books are listed in S1.5

In 2016, there are a growing number of Stillness Meditation teachers located in Victoria and some other States. Those living further afield may not have ready access to a Meares' teacher. Perhaps, travel combined with regular practice is an option. Even without travel one can still locate copies of Meares' books. Several were translated into many languages. The number in circulation is large - indicating that his method can be learnt if there is no accessible teacher. Progress might be slower but it can still be learnt[197].

Meares wrote:"[Stillness] *Meditation is something very simple... I am only pointing you in the right direction. The things that I have said are simply the signposts to point the way more clearly. **It is only in experiencing it that we come to understand it**.[198]..."a great many people have gone in the direction I have pointed, and have got there.... And now... they come up to me, and thank me for what they have achieved in the way of a better life"[199]*

---

196 Reardon, R Universal Reflections. Deakin Uni Press. 1993
197 McKinnon, P. Living Calm in a Busy World, p90
198 A Better Life, p126; bolding of last line in quote added
199 A Better Life, p114

CPSIA information can be obtained
at www.ICGtesting.com
Printed in the USA
BVHW030554050521
606419BV00005B/1038

9 780646 966939